A Princess Who Could Never Be

A Princess Who Could Never Be

The Untold Story of Mary Vetsera

Irene Colvin

NuDawn Publishing • Dallas

Published by:

NuDawn Publishing
10819 Myrtice Dr.
Dallas, Texas 75228

Photos in this book, including front cover photo, courtesy of the *Bildarchiv, Osterreichische Nationalbibiothek, Vienna.*

Library of Congress Catalog Card Number: 94-68856

ISBN: 0-9628093-0-6

Printed in the United States of America

In memory of the six children of Mary Vetsera who so bravely upheld the secret oath of silence that was so viciously put upon them and to the memory of their precious love that endured all. In addition, shall I never forget Gus Bauerlein, the investigative reporter I hired, who incessantly struggled to unearth some of the truth set forth within these pages.

Baroness Mary Alexandrine Vetsera during the time she attended the Polish Ball.

CONTENTS

Mary Vetsera as she may have been attired at the time of her arrival at Mayerling on the fateful day.

PUBLISHER'S NOTE

EVENTS OF THE PAST HAVE BEEN LONG SINCE ETCHED FIRMLY into the pages of history. Yet this does not mean that, in some instances, what is displayed in history books has not been (inadvertently or deliberately) misshapen. A case in point is the tale of Baroness Mary Alexandrine Vetsera.

The real story is a dramatic one and it reads like a work of fiction. In fact, it was suggested that this work be marketed as fiction. But that wouldn't have been fair because it is not, at least in the basic sense, a fabrication.

However, the information had to be pieced together from interviews, conversations, and legal documents after years of detective work. Some portions, therefore, can only be considered conjecture. But rest assured, the story is related in as readable a form as possible without adding, subtracting, or otherwise altering major incidents of the account.

In essence, in a work of this nature, fact and fiction cannot be separated, yet the overall account is related the way it basically occurred, and the main point is brought firmly home that the Mayerling incident *was not* the result of a *double suicide*, but indeed a *political cover-up*, and that Mary Vetsera *survived.*

FOREWORD

After a century of dormancy, "The Untold Story Of Mary Vetsera" now rises from within the depths of Austrian aristocracy. This new awakening exposes scars of treachery, feigned death, and deceit from within the House of Hapsburg.

Author Irene Colvin, granddaughter of the late Mary Vetsera, has devoted over forty years of her life to unveiling the truth in the assassination of Crown Prince Rudolph and the exile and untimely death of her grandmother. Without her tireless pursuit for documented facts and physical evidence, this entombed portion of Austrian and American history would remain hidden from the world forever.

You are about to embark on an absorbing and exciting journey through time with Ms. Colvin. Although the Austrian archives is cluttered with previously accepted theories, "The Untold Story Of Mary Vetsera" reveals the true chain of events that occurred fore and aft the turn of the century.

Within this haunting tale, Ms. Colvin entwines the beauty and grace of Vienna with the harsh reality of pioneer life in America. Her desire for truth and compassion is apparent as she weaves her story amid the strong sinew of research, documentation, visual observation, and personal interviews.

The time has come for you to begin your journey. Ms. Colvin awaits your presence. Enjoy this intriguing story of times past as truth unfurls before you from within its pages.

P. J. Meltabarger

PREFACE

ALL MY EARLY LIFE, I HAD BEEN HEARING A FANTASTIC STORY from some of my family that I was descended from royalty, but believed that it was only idle gossip. It seemed too incredible to be true. Never would I have suspected that I would someday learn that my heritage was connected with the Baroness Mary Vetsera and the horrible tragedy at Mayerling, and that I would become fascinated with the subject.

As my interest built, I began to satisfy my inquisitiveness by asking family members what they knew of this. Some were heedful not to reveal much; others freely presented what they knew. That's when I learned the truth: My grandmother Mary Vecera, who died in Muldoon, Texas in 1906, was none other than the Baroness Mary Vetsera, who had been deported from Austria in 1889 and altered her name to remove her link from a tragic past, preserving the secret that Crown Prince Rudolph had been assassinated.

From that time on I hungered to gobble up every new fact I could find on her life in an effort to prove she did not die at Mayerling and that the incident was a double-suicide-cover-up ordered by Emperor Franz Josef which forced the exile of all those directly involved. During a period spanning more than forty years, I have talked with private detectives, professors, graphologists, and other professionals regarding the subject. One graphologist was satisfied that Mary's signature on a letter dated 1906 originated from the same hand as a signature on a picture in Vienna signed in 1886—a mere three years before her assumed death. (A copy of that photograph appears on the front cover of this book.) Another graphologist agreed, but would not publicly admit it for fear of involvement.

A professor at the University of Texas, doctor of forensic science, examined photos of the Empress Elizabeth in Austria and photos of my great grandmother taken in LaGrange, Texas. His findings were that they were positively of the same person. He also made a study of a picture of Josef Bradfisch in Vienna and one of Ben Freidrich that I have in my family photo album. Without a doubt, he said they were of the same person. In addition, a photograph of Countess Larisch and Marie (as she was called in America), he identified as that of the same lady. He, too, wished to avoid involvement and would not sign a document supporting these facts.

Additionally, my quest has taken me hundreds of miles throughout Texas to court houses, museums, churches, and cemeteries and I have interviewed not only relatives, but priests who were personally told of the truth by the persons exiled.

In Ganado, Texas, I actually spoke at length with Countess Larisch and Josef Bradfisch, who related some startling details—details on which this book is largely based.

I even journeyed to Vienna to visit the church where Mary Vetsera was baptized, the homes once occupied by the Vetsera and the Baltazzi families, the falsified grave of Mary Vetsera in Heilingenkreuz, and Rudolph's former hunting lodge, now a nunnery.

While I was in Vienna, I hired Gus Bauerlein, an investigative reporter. Through his extensive efforts, he collected documents, pictures, and answers from personal interviews with librarians, historians, and priests.

I took him with me when I interviewed a history professor in Baden, Dr. Herman Serservy, who personally spoke with the son of Bradfisch and from him learned the truth about what happened at Mayerling. Dr. Serservy penned many articles on Mayerling, but said he had never written about the truth because he feared for his life. He did, however, feel at the time that the matter had cooled down enough and revealed the truth to us. That conversation was taped.

In all, I have put together a picture album of 100 pages and have amassed numerous letters and official papers strongly indicating that Mary Vetsera was still alive after the shooting.

I also possess a number of other taped conversations with people who knew the family well, in addition to letters and taped conversations from most of Mary's children, my aunts, who willingly poured out of their hearts the information that should have been told so long ago, as well as their pleadings for me to find the truth before their deaths. And I felt I have, for the voices of silence have spoken.

I will never forget those many intimate and touching conversations. One particular visit stands out in my mind. I can still hear my Aunt Caroline in her high-pitched voice as we examined a photograph of Mary. "My poor Maminka," she related. "I loved her so." We talked about what a sad life my grandmother must have had and reminisced until we were overcome with emotion.

There were many other enlightening experiences that I had with the family too numerous and detailed to mention here. I can only say that I am grateful to them for all that they revealed.

The project has been a tedious and lengthy, as well as challenging experience, but I can safely say that I am the world's expert on what really happened at Mayerling—and its after effects. Now, with great satisfaction, I eagerly present the true story to you.

INTRODUCTION

HISTORY DEPICTS THAT ON JANUARY 29, 1889 AT THE IMPERIAL hunting lodge of Maylering near Vienna, the Crown Prince Rudolph of Austria and the Baroness Mary Vetsera died in a double-suicide pact. It was suggested that they might have been despondent because their love relationship was forbidden or perhaps because Rudolph's political career was being stifled. But the facts were shrouded in mystery and the truth was never established—not, that is, until now.

Secrets that have been preserved for over 100 years have recently brought to light the startling truth about this momentous event. As it turned out, Emperor Franz Josef, Rudolph's father, had *ordered his son assassinated* because of torridly opposing political views and because he had bitterly objected to the love affair. But the plan, carried out with a pistol and disguised as a double-suicide, backfired when Mary survived the shooting.

"A Princess Who Could Never Be" exposes the facts surrounding the Mayerling cover-up and presents the story of its aftermath, a chronicle of Mary's new life—a life very few knew existed until now. From her harrowing deportment to her last days at Muldoon, Texas, from Indian raids to the loss of her hearing, it is a life of bravery and hopelessness, a life touched by love and fraught with hardship.

It is also the story of the survival of the people most closely involved, a scenario that was perhaps more devastating to them than Mayerling itself. Elizabeth, the pipe-smoking

Empress of Austria; Countess Larisch, the most faithful of cousins; Bradfisch renown for his patented whistling; and Agnes, the maid whose middle name could have been "devotion," were all destined to live in ruin, in exile with changed identities, separated from their families and afraid for their lives daily. Worst of all was the mental torture of never being able to reveal the secrets that haunted them almost to their graves.

No true story could be more dramatic and heart-rending. It has waited far too long to surface. But now, at last, the record has been set straight.

CHARACTERS INVOLVED

(and name changes in America)

Baroness Mary Vetsera (Mary Vecera): Daughter of Baron Johann Albin Vetsera and Empress Elizabeth of Austria. Preferred the name Mary but was sometimes referred to as Maria and occasionally as Marie. Adopted by Johann and Helene Vetsera. Died on Christmas day in 1906.

Crown Prince Rudolph Hapsburg: Crown Prince of Austria. Conspired against father for the Hungarian throne. Assassinated in 1889 at Mayerling.

Empress Elizabeth (Frances): Empress of Austria and queen of Hungary. Had illegitimate daughter, Mary, by Johann Vetsera. Died in LaGrange, Texas in 1928 at age of 91.

Countess Marie Larisch: Cousin of Rudolph befriended by Empress Elizabeth, implicated in the Mayerling tragedy. Exiled to Texas for her safety, where she dropped reference to her political title. Died in Ganado, Texas.

Baron Johann Albin Vetsera (John Vecera): Diplomat in Austrian government for 17 years. Father of Mary. Exiled to Texas in 1881. Died in LaGrange in 1910.

Baroness Helene Baltazzi Vetsera: Wife of Johann Vetsera. Adopted husband's illegitimate child Mary. Died in Austria in 1926.

Franz Josef of Austria: Emperor of Austria and King of Hungary. Had one son, crown prince Rudolph. Died in 1916 in Austria.

Josef Bradfish (Bennedict Freidrich): Rudolph's coachman. Ordered by the Emperor to assassinate Rudolph. Exiled to America. Died in Ganado, Texas.

Agnes Hurtak (Annie): The Vetsera's maid in Europe. Came to America with Elizabeth and Mary. Died in 1942 and buried in Plum, Texas.

Mitzi Marie Kaspar: Rudolph's former mistress. Spied on Rudolph for the Emperor after his affair with Mary began. All those in the Kaspar family who were involved came to Texas to avoid controversy in Europe. Died in 1949. Buried in Ganado, Texas.

PART I

ASSASSINATION AND EXILE

HOUSE OF HAPSBURG

VIENNA
AUSTRIA

ONE

"Countess Marie Larisch, I must apologize for this early call," the cabby said nervously. "But my friend Josef Bradfisch insisted that I deliver this letter to you immediately."

"Thank you," the Countess replied as she accepted the envelope.

Glancing down at it, she saw the crest, the official seal of the Crown Prince Rudolph Hapsburg. Her hands trembled as she walked into the study, closed the door, and carefully opened the envelope.

The message was written on Rudolph's personal stationary.

> Get Baroness Mary Vetsera from the Vetsera Mansion. Take her to the back of Rodecks. Bradfisch, my cabby, will be there with my carriage. He will drive her to Mayerling. I will be at the lodge waiting for her. She must come alone. I must talk to her immediately. It is urgent that I see her today!

His signature was boldly scrawled beneath the instructions. Countess Larisch looked away from the decree for a moment.

"It is most urgent that I see her today!" she whispered. "It sounds a bit ominous."

She read the note again and laid it down on the desk. The Countess slowly turned around and walked over to the window. Her gaze upon the rising sun was vacant, as though in a state of shock.

"Urgent," she murmured.

The Countess brushed a strand of hair back and slowly shook her head. Worry clouded her eyes as she returned to the desk and picked up the note.

It is quite possible, she thought, *that this is a serious meeting between cousin Rudolph and Mary. How could I have been so naive? For many months, I have helped arrange these clandestine engagements, but . . . Oh! What have I done? Was the appearance of innocence not so innocent?*

The Countess sat down and covered her pallid face with her hands.

Mary's constant reminders of proclaimed love for Rudolph, and the frequent decrees from Rudolph to deliver the Baroness to him was becoming a nightmare!

I have truly played a major role in their covert relationship, she thought. *They have shared their intimate feelings with me, allowing me to witness their tender glances, warm embraces, and farewell kisses. Perhaps I should have paid more attention.*

The Countess suddenly stood up. Her soft moan echoed against the silence of the room.

The Countess Marie Larisch understood all too well the heartbreak in an unhappy marriage. Empress Elizabeth, her aunt, had arranged for her to wed at a very young age. After much turmoil within the marriage, Countess Marie had abandoned her husband and family in Bohemia and relocated to Vienna. Although arranged marriages were customary, there was no consolation when the forced union by Empress Elizabeth failed. And thus the Countess had basked within the aura of love between Rudolph and Mary.

"Yes, it is true. The time has come to face their destiny," she hoarsely whispered. "The Crown Prince has to remain in his forced, unhappy marriage to Stephanie. It is urgent that he dismiss the Baroness from his life. . . .Oh, let Mary go? Poor Mary!"

"I will know more when Mary returns from Mayerling tomorrow," she sighed. "But now, I must hasten to do his bidding."

The Countess squared her shoulders and walked from the study. The cabby was still standing in the doorway, politely awaiting additional instruction.

"May I be of further assistance, Countess Larisch?"

"Please forgive me. I did not intend to delay you," she apologized. "Yes, I do require your services. Please wait for me at the carriage. I will be ready in a moment."

Thirty minutes later, the horse-drawn carriage left the Grand Hotel and traveled down the streets of Vienna with Countess Larisch seated in the coach. Her emotions surged from compassion for her friend's frustration over her involvement.

So today, she thought angrily, *cousin Rudolph sends a cabby with a message before dawn! It is absolute madness! If this is merely a joke, I shall never forgive him. However, I have no choice but to obey and meet the demands of dear Aunt Elizabeth and Cousin Rudolph. Indeed, Countess Larisch, you have no choice.*

Upon arrival at the Vetsera Mansion on Salesianergasse, Countess Marie Larisch did not have a definitive plan for accomplishing her mission. However, the breathtaking beauty of the city of Vienna and the prominent Third District momentarily provided escape from reality.

Sunlight danced upon the soft hues of early morning as the Countess approached the manor. She paused beside the fountain. A Greek Goddess statue was veiled within a mist of cold, clear liquid. She closed her eyes, absorbing the sweet sound of the water pouring over the regal figure. The brief respite soothed her sick feeling of apprehension. After a moment, she opened her eyes and smiled.

"No matter what, duty calls and Bradfisch awaits us," she sighed.

Agnes, the maid, met her at the door and sleepily invited her inside.

"The Baroness has been up for some time now," she yawned. "I will tell her that you are here."

"That is not necessary, Agnes," the Baroness said as she entered the room. "How nice to see you, Countess Marie. Please come in. Agnes will serve us coffee in the atrium."

Agnes bowed her head and closed the tall, ornate door as the Baroness and Countess left the vestibule. Moments later, the two ladies were relaxing in the cheerful splendor of the atrium. The alluring melody of Schubert's Sonata drifted from the music room. The haunting composition from the piano unified the scene with serenity.

"Countess, you are certainly out early this morning," the Baroness smiled.

The Countess smiled and winked.

"Yesterday I was having a problem with cold weather blues," she said. "I am hoping that a day with the dressmaker will cheer me up."

"Perhaps it will," the Baroness agreed.

"I thought Mary may enjoy accompanying me."

"If she feels up to it, I will agree with the outing. She has not been feeling too well," the Baroness responded.

Suddenly the music stopped, and Mary entered the room. Her presence added a radiance of youthful beauty and enthusiasm to the atrium. Her long black hair, beautiful, expressive eyes, and fair complexion was indeed comparable to her grace and charm.

"Countess Marie, what a pleasant surprise! I am delighted to see you."

"Please forgive my impulsive intrusion at such an early hour," Countess Larisch replied with a smile.

Then she softly added, "You are quite talented at the piano, Mary. I have enjoyed listening to you."

"My music instructor is coming today, so I thought perhaps I had better practice a bit," Mary said.

"Would you consider sacrificing your piano lesson this morning? I am hoping you will agree to join me in a day of leisure."

Mary's eyes widened with excitement.

"Yes!" she exclaimed. "Oh yes!"

She turned to her mother.

"Oh, Mama, may I please go with the Countess? You know how much I enjoy these outings! And I love the brisk air. It makes me feel so alive!"

The Baroness smiled.

"Yes, Mary. You may go. I have already given my permission to the Countess."

She dismissed the girl with the wave of one hand.

"Now go and prepare yourself for the jaunt. The Countess and I will finish our coffee and converse while we wait."

"Dress warmly," the Countess added in a loud voice as Mary raced up the stairs.

Moments later, Agnes entered the atrium with Sacher-torte and freshly brewed coffee. And, during the interim, the two ladies enjoyed pleasant conversation and the culinary fare.

During a brief lull in the visit, Countess Larisch breathed deeply and asked, "If the weather should worsen this afternoon, would you agree with Mary spending the night at my suite?"

She glanced down at her hands before adding, "I should have her home by mid-afternoon tomorrow."

The request was in essence nothing but a mere formality. There was no reason why the Baroness should refuse. She had certainly never mistrusted Countess Larisch's judgment.

That was just as well because before the Baroness could respond, Mary entered the atrium. The young lady was now attired in a dark green velvet suit and high topped lace boots.

Countess Larisch nodded in silent approval. She was glad Mary had chosen that apparel. It was Rudi's favorite.

Mary was breathless from the rapid modification and her two jaunts on the staircase.

"Should I wear my sealskin coat?" she gasped.

"Yes, of course, Mary," the Countess replied. "It should keep you quite warm."

Mary again raced up the staircase and returned momentarily with a black Russian mink hat and mittens. Her sealskin coat was draped over one arm.

Countess Larisch was keenly aware that precious time was slipping away regarding their appointed meeting with Bradfisch.

But discretion is a must, thought the Countess as she traced the delicate carvings on the arm of her chair. She watched as Mary casually stood in front of the mirror, adjusting her Russian mink bandit and positioning the black ostrich feather in a jaunty angle.

"Here, Mary," said Agnes. "Let me help you with your mittens. We don't want you to catch cold, now do we."

Soon the two young women were snugly seated within the coach.

"Where shall we go first?" Mary asked. Her eyes glistened with excitement as she waited for the response.

As the carriage moved forward and started down the parkway, Countess Larisch cleared her throat to speak.

"We should stop at the hotel for breakfast, I suppose," she smiled. "But I am afraid that my appetite was badly bruised by

Agnes offering me her delicious pastry. Perhaps we can plan for an early lunch?"

Mary agreed with a slight nod of her head.

"That will be . . ."

Suddenly the carriage bounced over a large cobblestone, jolting the two passengers. The Countess was startled to see that Mary had suddenly turned pale and grabbed her handkerchief. The girl quickly covered her mouth with the piece of white linen.

"Sorry, Countess Larisch," the cabby called. "It is impossible to miss all of the large stones."

"I understand, Driver. We are fine," the Countess called back.

She turned her attention back to Mary. The girl was as pale as her handkerchief.

Perhaps I should ask the coachman to take us back to the mansion, the Countess mused. But then she looked away when she realized that Mary was trying to hide her illness and amended her thought. *No, I must not do that! I will honor her by not asking any questions.*

She focused her attention on the leaf-barren trees, ornate statues, and beautiful structures that endeared her to the remarkable city of Vienna. A light snow was beginning to fall when she glanced again at Mary. Baroness Mary had regained her composure, and the handkerchief was no longer in sight.

"I am all right," Mary answered, "honestly." With a feeble laugh, she added, "Won't the shopkeepers be surprised to see us? We have never been on an outing at this hour in the morning."

The Countess conceded with a smile. The remainder of the journey was filled with the pleasant and lighthearted chatter from Mary.

Much too soon, however, the Countess realized the carriage was approaching the store Rodecks.

I must tell her the truth, thought Countess Larisch. *Now!*

She looked at Mary. The ambience of the pleasurable ride was instantly recast into a more somber mood.

"Mary, I have not been truthful with you. We will not be going to the boutique today."

Mary did not respond verbally, but her eyes reflected astonishment.

"Rudolph is waiting for you at Mayerling, Mary. I received a message early this morning. It is very important that he see you immediately. Bradfisch is waiting with the carriage."

"I don't understand," Mary stammered. "Rudi is at the lodge with friends. He cannot possibly want me there! And what is Bradfisch doing here if he took Rudi to Mayerling?"

"Bradfisch had a bad cold, so he could not take him. But now he is fine. He has been instructed to deliver you to the lodge without delay."

The Countess looked down. "I am sorry that I could not tell you earlier. I was instructed to get you to this point as quickly and quietly as possible."

Mary touched her friend on the shoulder.

"I understand, Countess Marie. You must do as Rudi demands without question."

"I feel it must be of vital consequence. Otherwise, why would he have you travel such a distance in this uncertain weather?" Countess Larisch paused before quietly adding, "If all goes well, Bradfisch will bring you back tomorrow, and I will have you returned home by afternoon."

"You are coming with me, aren't you, Countess?" Mary asked with a puzzled frown.

"No," Countess Larisch replied quietly. "This time Rudolph has asked only for you."

The Countess tried to offer a smile of encouragement for the young baroness, but the effort did not mask the unspoken concern in her eyes.

"Bradfisch will take good care of you, Mary. Do not worry. Have a safe and comfortable journey. I'll see you tomorrow."

The Countess quickly looked away lest Baroness Mary detect the overwhelming anxiety that had suddenly gripped her heart.

TWO

BRADFISCH OPENED THE DOOR OF THE CARRIAGE AS COUNTESS Larisch and Baroness Mary approached. He quickly assisted Mary inside, and the Countess covered her with additional blankets for the long, cold journey to the lodge.

"Thank you, Countess Marie," Mary whispered.

"You are quite welcome, my friend Baroness Mary. And please stay bundled up. It would not be fitting nor proper for the Crown Prince to receive a guest with consumption at his lodge, now would it?" She smiled and winked.

Mary giggled, and Countess Larisch stepped down from the coach.

"Bradfisch will bring you to this location tomorrow. I will be here with another carriage to take you home," she called as the coach door swung shut. "And have a safe journey."

Seconds later, the carriage sprang forward. Mary tried to wave a final farewell, but her arms were bound by the comforters. She sighed and leaned back against the seat.

I can't believe I am going to Mayerling to be with Rudolph, she silently pondered. *It seems as if I am dreaming*.

She looked around the interior of the coach and at her bundled up body.

"Yes!" she squealed and nestled down on the seat to savor the moment.

The snowfall was heavy and rapidly accumulating on the streets as the carriage raced through the city of Vienna. Mary sighed with contentment. Snow clung to the limbs of the trees, creating a very real winter wonderland.

"This still seems like a dream!" Mary murmured. "Everything happened so fast. If Rudi had not summoned me, I would be receiving my instruction on the piano right now." With a smile, she added, "But this is much more exciting."

The Baroness shivered and pulled the blankets tighter around her shoulders. "But the most wonderful part is that I will soon be with my love once again."

Suddenly a gust of wind hit the side of the carriage, and she realized the road was now icy. *Bradfisch is driving the horses awfully fast*, she thought. *It is so dangerous to push them this hard over the slick road.*

As the carriage careened through the countryside en route to Mayerling, the wind became a relentless force against the travelers. It whistled through the trees, creating a crackling sound that the Baroness found quite pleasing. She closed her eyes to listen to the haunting melody of nature, but a moment later she opened them again. The reverberation suddenly seemed eerie and ominous!

This is silly, Baroness Mary Vetsera, she silently chided. She sat up and watched the miles dissipate from their destination. The mountains around Badan and the Wienerwald were breathtaking with the majestic range blanketed in snow.

I am glad the sun is not showing through the clouds, she thought. *The glare from the snow and ice would be unbearable. I shall never forget when Rudi and I went bobsledding in weather about like this. It was also in the serene and beautiful woods near Vienna.*

Smiling with the memorable vision, Baroness Mary leaned her head back against the seat and closed her eyes. For a moment, she allowed herself to bask within the precious memory.

Discomfort suddenly brought her back to the present. Her face was stinging from the harshness of the Austrian winter storm. Shivering and shaking, she pulled the blankets higher. But this gesture exposed her legs to the bitter cold.

Rudi, why have you called for me? she pondered. *What could possibly be this urgent? Why must I make this journey in a snow storm?*

Moments later, her mind filled with a vision of Rudolph standing near the fireplace at the lodge. She imagined the warmth from his body pouring through her, filtering heat into every fiber of her being. For a golden moment, she absorbed the strength pouring forth from his loving embrace.

Doctor's report! Perhaps Rudi wants to speak to me about the doctor's report!

Mary sat up. Her eyes were now filled with dread and she began to weep. *Is this what Rudi wants to discuss? Will he ask me to get rid of the baby? Our baby? Otherwise, our secret will have to be revealed—and soon! Countess Marie may suspect anyway after my bout of sickness in the carriage this morning. I am thankful she did not ask any questions, but— Oh dear, what will Mama say? Or, even worse, Rudi's parents, the Emperor and Empress! Will I again be asked to leave the country? Oh, Rudi, what have we done?*

Without forewarning and much to Mary's surprise, the carriage suddenly came to a halt. Mary heard Bradfisch jump down, muttering to himself. She leaned out of the coach and saw him lift the front hoof of the horse on the right.

"Is everything all right?" she yelled above the howling wind.

"Yes, Baroness," Bradfisch shouted in a husky voice. "It's just that this horse lost a shoe, and now he is lame. I have to unhitch him. He can be replaced when we arrive at the Inn in Badan, but this is going to prolong our travel time."

Mary rested her head on the back of the seat and grumbled. Pain from the bitter cold crept through her legs and feet.

Countess Marie, I shall be forever grateful to you for the blankets. But I do wish you would have mentioned that I should wear ear muffs rather than this ostrich feather. It is not keeping my ears very warm.

She suddenly envisioned her neatly folded ear muffs tucked away inside the bureau drawer in Vienna. The mental comparison caused Mary to giggle.

When they reached the Inn, Bradfisch reined the horses to a halt. While the stable master exchanged the spent horses for a fresh team, Mary waited inside. The cheerful warmth of the fireplace and a sizable helping of hot food quickly revived both body and spirit for the youthful traveler.

Within a short time, the journey resumed, much faster now that the lame horse had been replaced. The warmth and contentment remained with the Baroness as the carriage raced through the dense winter weather. Once again enshrouded in blankets, she sighed and curled up in the corner of the seat. "I shall never forget traveling this same path last summer," she whispered. "with magnificent wildflowers in bloom across the hillsides, and the bright, colorful butterflies gracefully soaring amid the foliage."

As the wind driven snow pounded against the carriage, Mary smiled and snuggled within the blankets. She lost herself in the memory of the sweet scent of spring and the melodious song birds from one summer day. The aura of happiness did not fade as her thoughts turned to Rudolph and their baby.

And thus, the latter half of their journey to Mayerling passed quickly and quietly.

The muted light of day was fading when Mary glanced through the curtains.

"There it is!" she whispered. "We have arrived at Mayerling."

Her love for Rudolph swelled within her. With pulse racing and breath coming in short gasps, she watched the smoke drifting upward from the chimneys of the lodge. Staring at the scene before her, Baroness Mary Vetsera slowly removed the blankets from around her body.

THREE

COUNTESS MARIE LARISCH STOOD BESIDE HER CARRIAGE UNTIL Baroness Mary Vetsera disappeared from view. The feeling of dread and loneliness weighed heavy on her heart as the cabby assisted her into the coach. Seconds later, the carriage turned onto the street and started toward the Grand Hotel. The city of Vienna was beginning to awaken. Shopkeepers were opening their stores, and the rhythmic cadence of horse's hooves trotting down the streets echoed against the stately buildings. Countess Marie smiled and shook her head.

I am not going to spend the next twenty-four hours under a cloud of depression! she silently vowed.

"Driver, stop at the confectionery shop please!" she called, then reassured herself, "Chocolates are the perfect cure for worry. Baroness Mary is safe with Bradfisch, and winter will not last forever."

Countess Larisch enjoyed a sample of the chocolate during the return trip. She seemed unaware of the snowflakes that were rapidly accumulating along the roadway. When she walked up the steps to her door, a gust of wind compelled her to grab her hat, but her mind was at peace.

I have been acting as though this rendezvous between the Crown Prince and the Baroness is their first, she reflected. *How foolish of me!*

But the respite from distress was brief. When she went to bed that night, slumber was sporadic. She awoke the following morning exhausted. The dark circles beneath her eyes denoted a night filled with nightmarish visions.

I have the feeling that something dreadful has happened! Perhaps the carriage overturned in the storm. Mary may be badly injured or sick.

Suddenly Countess Marie felt jittery. She gasped and covered her mouth with her hand.

Yes, that is quite possible. It was quite obvious Mary was not feeling well yesterday morning!

She poured herself a cup of coffee and sat down at her writing desk.

"If I don't stop this incessant worrying, I will not be in any condition to deliver Mary to the Mansion this afternoon!" she reasoned. "In two hours I will be at the appointed meeting place and get Mary. It will be a great burden off me when she is safely home again!"

At precisely eleven o'clock, Countess Larisch walked through the lobby and requested a carriage. Within a short time, the driver reined the team to a halt behind Rodecks.

Countess Larisch sighed with contentment and leaned back against the seat of the coach. *How foolish of me to worry*, she thought. *Everything thus far is no different than numerous other engagements.*

The driver opened the door of the coach.

"Thank you," the Countess smiled, "but I am meeting someone here. I will wait in the coach until she arrives."

The cabby smiled and said, "Very well, Countess. Please let me know if you need anything."

"Thank you, I will. But truly I am quite comfortable."

Nearly one hour later, the bells from a distant cathedral echoed through Vienna, and the Countess felt tension again rise within her. *Twelve o'clock*, she reflected. *Bradfisch should be arriving with Mary any minute now.*

But unfortunately, the passage of time was not kind to the Countess. As the second hour of waiting approached, she heard the horses become agitated, restlessly stomping their hooves against the cobblestones and softly nickering. The door of the coach again opened.

"My team is getting nervous, Countess. Perhaps I could send another carriage for you?" the driver politely offered.

"No," she responded. "No, I think I will go back to the Grand Hotel and wait there. The weather may have delayed my party's arrival in Vienna and they will know where to go if I am not here."

"Very well," the driver replied and closed the door.

Upon arrival at the hotel, the Countess felt numb as she stepped from the carriage. She slowly walked through the lobby and up to her suite without acknowledging the salutations from the staff. She sat down on the settee in her room as though in a trance.

When the clock on the mantle chimed twice, she felt despair overwhelm her. She paced the floor with a white linen handkerchief clenched tightly within her hand.

"I should have gone with her," she scolded herself. "Something terrible has happened. I just know it!"

Suddenly she stopped pacing. Her eyes filled with terror, and she gasped.

Two days before Rudolph left for the lodge, he stated that he was uneasy about making this journey to Mayerling. Perhaps he too sensed danger!

The Countess shook her head.

No, that does not make sense. Why should this time be any different than numerous others? The Crown Prince is under the constant protection of guards. Besides, Rudi has lived his entire life with the possibility of danger. Threats of bodily harm are indisputable evils within royalty.

A loud rap on the door of her suite suddenly yanked the Countess back to the present.

"Perhaps Bradfisch has finally arrived with Mary!" she exclaimed.

Relief surged through her as she hurried toward the door. "How foolish of me to worry. Rudolph adores Mary, and he would most certainly make provisions for her safe return."

A quick glance in the mirror caused her to pause for a moment. She brushed her hair back with one hand and slapped her cheeks to regain a bit of color on her face.

Then she smiled and opened the door.

"Good afternoon, Countess Larisch. I hope you are feeling well today."

A servant was standing in the doorway with a parcel of clothing in his arms.

"The maid asked me to deliver your belongings. They are cleaned and pressed, but she sends her apologies. She was unable to bring them herself due to an emergency with her family."

The Countess felt her lips begin to tremble. Again, her body and soul was inundated with fear and disappointment. She forced a smile and accepted the belongings.

"I had forgotten that she was bringing them today," she said softly. "Please thank her and offer my condolence. I hope the emergency is of little significance."

"Yes, I will tell her, Countess. Have a good day."

The servant turned to leave. He hesitated and looked back at her.

"Are you feeling well, Countess? You look rather pale. Is there anything I can get for you?"

"No, I am fine. But, thank you for inquiring."

After closing the door, distress engulfed her. She leaned against the wall and moaned before slowly entering the bedroom to put away the garments.

The clock on the mantle chimed three times. Each peal of the hour thundered against the taut nerves of Countess Marie Larisch. As the last chime abated, she stood up and walked to the cloak closet and removed her coat. She quickly slipped it over her shoulders and left the suite. Hurriedly descending the stairs, she ran through the lobby. Her hands trembled, and her voice sounded distant and hollow as she advised the cabby of her intended destination—the Vetsera Mansion.

Her fingers tapped nervously upon the seat beside her as the wheels of the carriage creaked through the newly fallen snow. The journey seemed to last an eternity.

But, tension mounted even higher within the Countess as the Vetsera Mansion came into view. A cascade of emotions suddenly poured forth. Fear and dread of the unknown merged with the terror and guilt of reality. She sighed and covered her eyes for a moment.

It is time for the truth to be told, she silently vowed. *Mary may be in dire need of help . . . or perhaps it is too late!*

Countess Larisch stepped out of the carriage before it had come to a halt. She ran to the entrance and opened the door. She pushed Agnes aside as she stormed into the vestibule.

"I have to see the Baroness immediately!"

Agnes stared at the Countess in shocked disbelief.

"I have to speak to the Baroness," she repeated. "At once. Find her!" she screamed.

The Baroness stepped into the vestibule. She silently motioned for the Countess to enter the study. She followed the distraught Countess into the room and gently closed the door behind her.

"Sit down," the Countess demanded. "Please!"

Without shifting her gaze from Countess Larisch, the Baroness slowly seated herself on a chair.

"Now I must speak, and you must listen. Do not interrupt me."

The Baroness listened without interrupting as Countess Marie Larisch shared her fears and concern of the past twenty-four hours regarding the safety of Mary. Anger was mounting in the eyes of the Baroness.

"Why did you allow this to happen?" the Baroness shouted. "Why did you not go with her?"

"We now have no alternative," the Countess continued quietly. "We must go directly to the police."

Suddenly the Baroness stood up. Her body was rigid with fear and anger. Her response was crisp and with emotion.

"You are right, Countess," she said. "We have no alternative. Do you have the message from the Crown Prince with you?"

Countess Larisch softly said, "Yes, I do."

"Very well. We will go. The document should convince Baron Krauss to act quickly on this matter."

The carriage ride to the police station was shrouded in strained silence. The truth had drained the Countess, and she now sat immobile, staring straight ahead. She felt void of emotion, and her body was numb.

Likewise, the Baroness sat in silence as though in a state of shock. Neither lady moved until the carriage came to a halt in front of the Police Station.

Moments after their arrival, Baron Krauss laid the document down on his desk and shook his head.

"My apologies, Baroness Vetsera. But neither I nor my men can assist you."

Countess Larisch and Baroness Vetsera glanced at one another in shocked disbelief.

"But why?" the Baroness exclaimed. "I do not understand!"

"Mayerling is not within my jurisdiction," Baron Krauss explained. "It is not my district. I have no right to investigate unless I know for a fact that something serious has taken place."

"Would you be at liberty to just check on Mary?" the Baroness appealed.

"Just to make sure that she is all right?" the Countess asked.

Baron Krauss stood up and leaned over his desk.

"I am sorry," he said. "There is really nothing that I can do at this time. Mary's presence at the lodge does not grant us the right to interfere. Thus far, the situation is a private matter between Mary and Crown Prince Rudolph."

Baron Krauss walked around the desk and looked at each lady before again speaking.

"I will notify you immediately if any word is received from the lodge. Meanwhile, I urge you to go home and await further word from Mary or myself."

Tears streamed down the face of the Countess as the Baroness begged Baron Krauss for immediate assistance.

"Go now," the Baron said gruffly. "There is nothing more that I can do at the present time. Now please go before I request escorts to deliver you to your carriage!"

The journey back to the Vetsera Mansion was a nightmare for the two passengers. The driver was aware of the panic besetting Baroness Vetsera and Countess Larisch, and his whip lashed at the horses as they raced through the streets of Vienna. Sobs of distress echoed from within the coach as he reined the team to a halt at the entrance.

Baroness Vetsera and Countess Larisch did not speak nor look at one another as they entered the manor. Agnes met them at the door and aided with the removal of their coats.

"Send a messenger for my brother Alexander Baltazzi, my sister Countess Marie Stockau and her husband Count Georg Stockau. I request their presence at our home as soon as possible," Baroness Vetsera demanded of Agnes.

Turning to Countess Larisch, she added, "Come, Countess, we will wait in the study."

The Countess followed her into the dimly lit chamber. She quietly sat down and watched as the Baroness lighted a candelabra that was sitting on the fireplace mantle. The wicks slowly accepted the flame, casting eerie shadows about the room. The Countess shivered and held her breath until the light became a steady glow, and the phantom illusions settled into motionless shades of darkness.

None of this seems real, thought the Countess. She inhaled deeply.

She glanced at the Baroness before slowly exhaling. The matron was now seated at the writing desk, staring at her.

"Why did you request the presence of . . ."

The Countess was interrupted before she could complete her question.

"Count and Countess Stockau are Mary's Godparents," the Baroness declared. "Besides," she started to confess, "they are the ones aware of . . ."

Her voice trailed off into silence, and she looked down at her hands. Her palms were damp with perspiration, and she clasped them together to arrest the incessant trembling.

"Oh, I am glad that you sent for them," the Countess replied softly, paying no particular attention to Baroness Vetsera's last few words. She smiled and added, "Perhaps Mary will arrive soon, and they too can welcome her home."

This fleeting moment of hope filled the study with renewed optimism. The tension ebbed into calm as Countess Larisch saw the Baroness smile.

"I will have Agnes prepare coffee and cakes for our guests," the Baroness said. "Mary will *also* appreciate the gesture when she returns from her long journey."

After Baroness Vetsera left the room, Countess Marie was wringing her hands as she slowly walked to the fireplace. She stared at the flames from the candles for a long moment.

"My mouth speaks of Mary's safe arrival, but my heart echoes in terror for her timely return. Will this nightmare never end?"

A tear slid down her cheek and settled on the bodice of her dress. Then hearing footsteps approach the study, she brushed the dampness from her face, and, as Baroness Vetsera again entered the room, she forced a smile.

FOUR

THE TICKING CADENCE OF THE CLOCK IN THE STUDY SOUNDED hollow as the hours slowly slipped away. Alexander Baltazzi suddenly stood up and cleared his throat. He walked to the fireplace and cleaned the ashes from his pipe.

"I will honor you and your evasive answers regarding Mary's journey to Mayerling," he said. "But, I do feel that you should prepare yourself for future scrutiny on the issue. As you know, Baroness, the whole of Vienna has been questioning the relationship between the Crown Prince and Mary for some time now"

Baroness Vetsera and Countess Larisch glanced at one another.

"I understand, Brother, and I agree. But now is not the time to . . ."

As a strong gust of wind rattled the windowpanes, the Baroness suddenly covered her face with her hands.

Countess Stockau walked over to her and sat down. She gently hugged the Baroness before speaking in a loud and clear voice.

"I believe I speak for all of us when I say that Mary will soon be home. Perhaps she will be a bit tired and hungry, but nevertheless, our young baroness will be arriving shortly."

Murmurs of agreement filled the chamber with optimism. The burden of uncertainty seemed to vanish, and the five denizens momentarily breathed a sigh of relief. Count Stockau joined Alexander near the fireplace, and the two men began conversing over items of national interest. Countess Larisch sat down with the Baroness and Countess Stockau. The tone of her lighthearted conversation validated their newborn confidence.

A moment later, the tranquility was shattered by a thunderous rap on the entrance door.

The little group in the study listened as Agnes responded to the summons. Seconds later, Officer Habrada and Officer Wysposill of the Special Police entered the room.

The tension soared to new heights as Officer Habrada began to speak. His voice was deep, and his words were articulate.

"A tragedy of international magnitude occurred at Mayerling last evening," he said. "Our Crown Prince Rudolph Hapsburg is dead! However, I am very pleased to report that Mary survived. There was a shooting incident at the lodge that involved both Crown Prince Rudolph and Baroness Mary."

Officer Habrada looked at Baroness Vetsera.

"Mary has a bullet wound to the head, but the Court Physician assures us that she will live."

For a brief moment, shock paralyzed the party of five. Then screams and moans rumbled throughout the mansion. The staff of servants were thrust into a state of panic as the news traveled through the ambiance of elegance. Baroness Vetsera recoiled as though struck by a hand. She gasped and tumbled forward, her limp body falling across a chair. Countess Larisch was unable to hear the chaos. A deafening roar swept through her head, dulling her senses. She gazed vacantly about the room as though in a trance. Countess Stockau emitted a low moan and reeled backward. Sobs of anguish poured forth from her trembling body. Alexander and Count Stockau stood silent and unmoving. They seemed etched of stone and frozen in time.

Countess Larisch stumbled toward the unconscious Baroness.

"Agnes," she screamed. "Come quickly!"

She fell to her knees beside the matron.

Agonizing moments lapsed before self-control again surfaced among those in attendance. The air was charged with tension, but the three women and two men were now rational and anxious to receive word about Mary. Officer Habrada cleared his throat and continued.

Rustling movement and murmurs of dread broke the stillness.

Questions rumbled through the chamber. Officer Habrada raised his hand to silence them.

"We have reason to believe our Crown Prince Rudolph and Baroness Mary Vetsera were consummating a suicide pact."

Again nervous rustling and hushed sorrow coursed through the assembly. Countess Larisch raised her forefinger to her lips.

Officer Habrada looked at each one present before speaking.

"A gun was found near the potential suicide victims," he said in a rattled voice.

He walked over to Baroness Vetsera, gently lifted her chin, and gazed into her eyes.

"Mary's presence at Mayerling suggests of a more intimate relationship than mere friends."

He clasped his hands behind his back and returned to the center of the room.

"Baroness, I cannot stress enough the importance of discretion regarding this disaster. A scandal against the House of Hapsburg must be avoided. Emperor Franz Josef's Prime Minister, Count Edward Von Taaffe, has issued a decree stating that Mary be sent from Austria immediately."

Gasps of protest forced the officer to again raise his hand for silence.

"Her presence in the city of Vienna would only aggravate public suspicion of her involvement in this incident. Suspicion regarding the death of Crown Prince Rudolph will forever follow Mary Vetsera. It is imperative that she leave the country at once!"

Countess Larisch was pallid and shaking as she stumbled to a chair and sat down beside Agnes. Her body trembled with guilt and fear as she buried her face in her hands. She quietly wept.

"Mary?" Baroness Vetsera shouted. "Shot? Suicide? My Mary banished from Austria?"

Suddenly the Baroness stood up. Her eyes were filled with horror as she stared at Officer Habrada.

With trembling lips, she shouted, "No! You will not take my Mary away from me!"

"It is with deepest regret, Baroness Vetsera," Officer Habrada said, "but there is no question regarding Mary leaving Vienna immediately."

He paused before adding, "And you, Baroness, are indeed the logical person to accompany her."

The Baroness started to speak, but the officer again raised his hand.

"Mary's injury will require special attention for quite some time. She will soon be on board a ship en route to America. And it has been strongly suggested that you, Baroness, and your maid Agnes sail with her. The extent of Mary's injury is still uncertain, and she may require more assistance than you are able to provide."

Baroness Vetsera inhaled and sat down on the edge of her chair. Officer Habrada paused only a moment before continuing.

"Count Von Taaffe's decree orders that you and others near you aid in Mary's departure."

With hands once again clasped behind his back, Officer Habrada paced across the room several times. Then he turned to Alexander and Count Stockau.

"Officer Wysposill and I are going to Mayerling now, and I suggest that you both accompany us."

Alexander and Count Stockau glanced at one another before abruptly nodding in approval.

Officer Habrada acknowledged their response with a nod and resumed pacing.

"Count Von Taaffe further proclaims that everyone here take a vow of silence. Not one word regarding this incident shall be spoken beyond this room until further notice. Do you all understand the importance of this mandate?"

Officer Habrada paused to study the reaction from each person present: Baroness Vetsera, Countess Marie Larisch, Agnes, Alexander Baltazzi, and Count and Countess Stockau.

He did not shift his gaze from each one until fully satisfied with their affirmation.

"Agnes," Officer Habrada said, "you are most familiar with Mary's wardrobe. Gather the items that you feel she will need for the voyage to America. Do so immediately. We will take them with us to Mayerling."

The maid stood up to comply with the order.

"Remember to get her long mink coat, Agnes" Countess Larisch said softly. "It may be cold during the voyage."

"And don't forget her black Russian hat," Baroness Vetsera added quietly. "It may conceal the bandages on her head."

The moon was sinking low on the western horizon as Special Police Officers Habrada and Wysposill carried Mary's wardrobe trunk to the carriage. Alexander and Count Stockau waited until the Special Police coach passed through the main gate before following the lead carriage through the white veil of winter to the lodge.

Baroness Vetsera, Countess Larisch, and Countess Stockau stepped back into the vestibule as the two horse-drawn rigs disappeared from view. Agnes closed the door and turned to Baroness Vetsera.

"Will that be all for the night?" The tone of her voice was automatic, dull, and void of emotion.

"Yes, Agnes. Try to get some rest." The Baroness paused before adding, "For we know not what the new day may bring."

"Do you mind, Baroness," Countess Stockau asked, "if I retire to the guest quarters for a while? I need some time alone to absorb the evening's events."

"Please do, my dear sister. And I hope you will one day forgive me for involving you and the Count in this strange twist of fate."

"We must think only of Mary," Countess Stockau replied quietly. "As her Godmother, her pain and confusion is mine also. She must be terribly frightened now, and we must be strong for her."

Countess Larisch slowly walked back into the study. She sat down in a chair that was partially hidden within the shadows of the room.

"Dead? What an ugly and forever word! Oh, what a dreadful tragedy," she wept hysterically. "Even as children, we were more than mere cousins. Rudi was my friend. I cannot believe that he is dead! I will never again see his love for life that glistened in his clear blue eyes nor hear the rich tone of his laughter. Never! Never will I be by his side again."

Suddenly the Countess put her hand on her forehead, and a faint smile appeared on her lips. *Perhaps he is not dead! If he and Mary ran away, they could openly share their love. Perhaps they thought that a feigned death would be a good plan to procure their united happiness!*

A moment later, her shoulders slumped, and a low groan echoed through the muted chamber.

No. I dream of nought but fantasy. Crown Prince Rudolph Hapsburg is indeed deceased. And Baroness Mary Vetsera is indeed at the lodge, wounded and awaiting deportation from Austria. And I, Countess Marie Larisch, am guilty of assisting in their tragic kismet!

Nestled within the shadows of pre-dawn, the Countess quietly grieved alone for the loss of her cousin. She mourned for her role as liaison to sanctify the two young lovers.

As footsteps approached the study, she sat up and daubed the tears from her face. Her delicate fingers smoothed the folds of her long dress as she awaited the arrival.

The Countess watched in silence as Baroness Vetsera entered the room and sat down at the writing desk. The matron's face was pale and etched with worry. Her eyes appeared glazed, void of life.

Countess Larisch inhaled deeply and rose to her feet. She stepped quietly across the room and paused beside the matron.

"Baroness," she said softly. "I understand the pain you must be feeling at this moment. My heart is heavy with the loss of the Crown Prince, and I grieve for our dear Mary."

The Countess embraced the Baroness and sat in the chair nearest the desk.

"I have been aware of the bond between Crown Prince Rudolph and Mary for some time now," she confessed. "In truth, I have served as liaison, transporting messages of love between the two of them and arranging each discreet rendezvous."

Baroness Vetsera listened in silence as the Countess meticulously weaved a tale of romance and devotion. She portrayed the lovers as pure and flawless, a perfect union of body and soul.

"Their love for one another was intense and eternal." She paused before quietly adding, "Indeed, a suicide pact between

Crown Prince Rudolph and Baroness Mary Vetsera is plausible."

Baroness Vetsera suddenly sprung from her chair. The force of her action upset the seat. Her eyes blazed with malice.

"It is your fault!" she shouted. "I entrusted my daughter to you, Countess, and you betrayed me. Mary's life is ruined! Our lives are ruined!"

The matron brushed against a figurine on her desk. Suddenly, she hit it. Then she stared at the shattered remnants on the floor without moving. Her shoulders slumped, and tears streamed down her face. She stumbled to the settee and sat down.

"Forgive me Countess Larisch," she said. "I should not place blame upon you. Condemnation is of no use to us now."

The Countess sighed and looked down at her hands. Somehow the outburst had relieved the pressure of intense guilt.

"Thank you, Baroness, but my shame will forever leave a scar. My grace lies only in my lineage of aristocracy."

Countess Larisch sat down beside Baroness Vetsera and gently covered the matron's hands with her own. The two Austrian ladies of nobility quietly wept for the tragic death of an era.

And thus, truth began to rise above the gray cloak of obscurity.

FIVE

SUNLIGHT DANCED UPON THE NEWLY FALLEN SNOW AS THE Vetsera carriage traversed through the streets of Vienna en route to the Palace to pay homage to the Empress. The chestnut team was brushed and manicured to perfection, and the decorative brass on the carriage and harness was polished to a radiant luster. The scene was a magnificent portrait of Austrian nobility quietly surveying the beauty of an ivory land of enchantment. But the mood within the coach disclosed grim reality.

"We are doing right by visiting Empress Elizabeth," Baroness Vetsera acknowledged.

"Yes, I know," replied Countess Larisch. "It is proper for us to convey our condolences to the mother of the deceased Crown Prince. And I do love Aunt Elizabeth. I just," the Countess paused. "I just don't know what to say."

"Nor do I," the Baroness sighed. "Nor do I."

With somber expression, the doorman ushered the ladies into the palace and announced their presence. Empress Elizabeth did not move or acknowledge them for a moment. Her face was ashen. Dark circles underscored her large bloodshot eyes. She was smoking her pipe with one hand and clutching a handkerchief tightly in the other.

Without looking at the two guests, Empress Elizabeth said with trembling voice, "My son Rudolph has been taken from me, and my daughter Mary has been seriously wounded."

Countess Larisch gasped and reeled backward. She seized the arm of Baroness Vetsera for support, but her eyes remained riveted on the Empress.

"Forgive me, Empress," the Countess whispered. "For a moment I thought you said . . ."

"You were correct, Countess," the Empress declared in a strong and forceful voice.

She puffed on the pipe for a moment before adding, "There is no reason now to deny the truth. Mary is indeed my daughter!"

Empress Elizabeth shifted her attention to the matron standing beside her niece.

"Baroness Vetsera, please tell Countess Larisch the truth. It has been buried within the facade of virtuous nobility too long. The time has come for her to fully understand the House of Hapsburg."

The Baroness said, "I agree, Your Highness. I will tell her everything after our departure from the Hofburg Palace."

The Empress gave her a brief nod and laid her pipe down.

"Please, sit down," she murmured.

As she turned away, Baroness Vetsera and Countess Larisch sat down upon the gold brocade settee. They watched Empress Elizabeth pace across the ornate room twice before coming to a halt in front of them.

"Baron Krauss insisted the catastrophe at Mayerling was a suicide pact between Rudolph and Mary."

She pressed the handkerchief to her brow and sighed.

"In truth, my son was murdered. The clandestine courtship of Rudolph and Mary was a perfect cover-up for the political assassination, which had been plotted by Emperor Franz Josef."

Countess Larisch heard the words, but the voice of the Empress sounded distant, echoing against the shallow realm of reality. She felt light-headed, and she took several deep breaths to diminish the dizziness. She couldn't believe that

Baroness Vetsera had known all along of their kinship, and yet had said nothing to her!

Why? the Countess thought, *Oh dear God, why?* She leaned forward, hoping to regain control of her emotions.

The voice continued.

"As you know, Baroness, your excursions to Paris and London with Mary did not lessen their love for one another. Last week Emperor Franz Joseph summoned Rudolph to the palace. After a final plea to terminate the relationship, the Crown Prince became outraged and refused. His father had no recourse. It was imperative that he reveal the blood kinship of the Crown Prince and Baroness Mary, that of being half brother and sister."

Empress Elizabeth walked over to the fireplace and gazed at a portrait of the Emperor that was suspended above the mantle. Neither Baroness Vetsera or Countess Larisch moved or spoke as they watched her slowly leave the painting and walk to the window.

"There is more," she said quietly.

The Countess and the Baroness glanced at one another.

"Indeed," Empress Elizabeth sighed, "there is more."

Countess Larisch held her breath as the attractive lady of nobility walked back across the room and sat down near them.

"Crown Prince Rudolph not only expressed his eternal love for Mary to Emperor Josef," she said, "but he also proclaimed that the situation was not their fault. He bitterly exclaimed that they should have been informed about their blood relation many years ago. Numerous times, he expressed concern for their baby."

"Their baby?" Baroness Vetsera whispered as she turned to the Countess.

"I did not know . . ."

Countess Larisch suddenly recalled Mary, hiding her "ill-ness" in the carriage on the morning of her departure. The incident was an apparition of truth!

Empress Elizabeth cleared her throat and stood up.

"Several days ago, Emperor Josef stated that radical measures would be taken to prevent further scandal to the Hapsburg throne. And today we mourn the death of our Crown Prince."

Countess Larisch watched in silence as the regal matron fought for self-composure.

"The past few days have been a nightmare! I was told by the Emperor to stay out of it."

Moments later, the Empress said, "I believe coffee is in order, my dear Baroness Vetsera and Countess Larisch. Do you agree?"

Both ladies nodded in agreement.

"I informed the servants that we were not to be disrupted. Please forgive my absence for a moment while I tell them of our need."

As Empress Elizabeth departed from the room, neither the Countess or the Baroness spoke. They did not even look at one another during her brief absence.

Soon the Empress returned, followed by several servants who poured coffee into elaborate vessels and offered culinary hospitality to the Baroness and the Countess. As the room cleared of palace staff, Empress Elizabeth turned to Baroness Vetsera.

"Baron Krauss mentioned that you should accompany Mary to America. I have given this a lot of thought, and I disagree. I will go with my daughter, but you must also leave Vienna for a time to insure your safety from the raging public. I have sent word to Count Von Taaffe regarding the change in plans. I maintained that you be allowed to return to Vienna as soon as possible."

Baroness Vetsera slowly bowed her head. Empress Elizabeth continued in a calm and matter-of-fact voice.

"Baron Krauss insists that you remain absent from Vienna for several months. He has agreed to delay granting information to the reporters, and this will insure our safe departure."

Countess Larisch shook her head in disbelief.

"We have taken an oath of silence with Officer Habrada as decreed by Count Von Taaffe. It will be very hard to honor this through the upcoming onslaught of rumors and false reports."

Baroness Vetsera suddenly rose from her chair. She walked over to the window, paused briefly, and strode back across the room.

"Empress Elizabeth, are you seriously considering leaving the country with Mary?"

The Empress bowed her head.

"My only son is gone! And Mary, my daughter, has been forced into exile! My life in Vienna will be empty and meaningless. I indeed will accompany my daughter to America. I have traveled extensively for years, and thus my absence from Vienna will be of no consequence to the House of Hapsburg or Austria. Besides, I will find relief in the change."

"Relief?" echoed Baroness Vetsera and Countess Larisch.

"I truly loved Emperor Franz Josef throughout our courtship and the first years of our marriage. But, within a short time, I began to hear rumors of his faltering devotion for me. For years, he and I remained friends rather than united as man and wife. He is no longer my friend."

Empress Elizabeth paused before quietly adding, "I have been searching for escape, and destiny now offers my release. I prefer living in hiding as a commoner, rather than tolerating the disgrace concealed within the walls of the Palace."

She glanced at the ladies and a faint smile appeared on her lips.

"I will, however, miss the sweet mountain air of Reichenau and the breathtaking Isle of Corfu."

For a short time, the room was cast in a veil of silence as the three ladies reflected on their discussion thus far. Suddenly, the Countess stood up.

"Your Highness, there is something you must know. I too have been involved in this scandal."

The Empress looked at her niece and raised her brow.

"Oh? In what way, Countess?"

Countess Larisch found herself repeating her role as liaison for the second time. She was breathless when she concluded.

"I am guilty," she wept. "And I now realize that the message from Crown Prince Rudolph was falsified. He did not request Mary's presence at the lodge. It was all a part of the plot to assassinate him and our Baroness Mary. How could I have been so naive!"

"My dear niece," the Empress quietly declared, "I am so sorry you have been a victim in this."

She shook her head thoughtfully.

"Since you are involved, Countess, you must leave with Mary and me. Your life would be in grave danger if you remained in Austria."

"But my family is in Bohemia," Countess Larisch protested. "Will I never see them again?"

"You must decide your destiny, Countess Marie. You now know of the dangerous risk should you decide to remain."

Empress Elizabeth turned to the Baroness who had patiently listened throughout the confession.

"Thank you, Baroness, for adopting my child. You have granted her the tender love and care that she so well deserved. It is tragic that I did not share the truth with Rudolph and Mary. You vowed to secrecy, and you maintained that promise. And now I must attempt to redeem my daughter with truth."

Wind whispered against the Hofburg Palace, and scattered snowflakes clung to the windowpanes. The past forty-eight hours had dramatically and eternally altered the lives of each lady. Their silence now spoke of acceptance in change and deliverance from doom.

"I caution you not to take a wardrobe befitting a countess," Empress Elizabeth suddenly said. "In my case, Emperor Josef will conceal my lengthy departure from Vienna with a tale of mourning for my deceased son. But we must change our appearance to that of commoners."

"And," she turned to Baroness Vetsera. "You must return to the mansion and pack the balance of Mary's belongings. Secure as much currency as possible. I do not know the extent of her injury, and we may encounter unexpected expenses. And, we must keep in mind that jewelry or other valuables could be traced back to our identities and location."

As Empress Elizabeth stood up, Baroness Vetsera and Countess Larisch followed suit.

"Now you must go. There is much to be done before our departure."

"Yes, Your Highness, there is much to be done. And so little time . . . " the Countess whispered.

The three ladies of nobility embraced one another and silently walked through the splendor of the Hofburg Palace.

Baroness Vetsera and Countess Larisch stepped into the coach. Neither of them spoke as the driver reined the team through the ornate wrought iron entrance. The carriage slowly and silently traversed amid the snow encased gardens and passed by the myriad of graceful statues. The Ringstrasse was bustling with elaborate carriages and ladies in exquisite fashion being escorted by men of distinction. Countess Larisch sighed.

"It seems so strange to see people attired in their finest, engaging in a night with the masterful music of Johann Strauss. Our world has been transformed forever, and they are not yet aware of the tragedy."

"Tomorrow," the Baroness whispered. "Tomorrow the city will learn of the tragic so-called suicide pact, and the death of Crown Prince Rudolph Hapsburg."

"Baroness," Countess Marie said quietly. "Why did you adopt Mary after rearing two children of your own?"

Baroness Vetsera leaned her head against the back of the seat and closed her eyes.

"Since you were her confidante," she answered, "I am really surprised the Empress never told you. Mary's father is Baron Vetsera, yes, my late husband. Because of Elizabeth's long absences, Emperor Franz Josef could not be persuaded into believing that he was the father. He rejected the unborn sibling and ordered Elizabeth to take an extended journey until after the birth of the baby. During her isolation, Elizabeth asked that Baron Vetsera and I rear their child as our own. My husband, wanting this child, begged of me to accept her. At first, I said no, for the shock of him committing adultery was devastating to me. It took quite some time for me to adjust to the idea."

Countess Larisch gasped and touched the hand of the Baroness. Baroness Vetsera gently patted the Countess on the shoulder.

"Yes, Countess, it was a very difficult decision. But, after a period of time, I was able to forgive my husband and Elizabeth."

"Did you know Elizabeth at the time?"

"She was a casual acquaintance, not a close friend," the Baroness replied.

"How were you able to keep the exchange a secret?"

The Baroness shook her head and sighed.

"The Baron had been planning a trip to Russia for quite some time. Thus I was able to quietly go with him. The exchange was a rather dramatic scene," the Baroness smiled. "A coachman dressed in dark clothes and a black cloak arrived at Elizabeth's hideaway. The baby was quickly passed to two nuns riding in the carriage. The phantom rig immediately disappeared into the darkness of the night. The tiny princess was then taken to the chapel where my husband Johann and I proceeded to finalize the adoption. Six months after leaving

Russia, we returned to Vienna with our baby. Count and Countess Stockau were the only ones present at Mary's baptism."

"That is why you requested their presence last night!" the Countess said.

"Yes, they have been aware of Mary's lost birthright since the adoption."

Countess Larisch was silent for a moment. Visions of times past rose from the depths of latent memories.

"This explains my Aunt Elizabeth's interest in the Vetsera family!" she quietly exclaimed. "She was forever asking me questions, especially about Mary, when I would return from a visit at your home."

Baroness Vetsera looked at the Countess. A lone tear rolled down her cheek and fell unchecked onto the bodice of her coat.

"But," Countess Larisch continued, "if you knew that Rudolph and Mary were half brother and sister, why did you not tell me?"

"We took a vow of silence," Baroness Vetsera said. "No one was to speak of the incident ever again. I was unable to tell you even after learning of your close relationship to the Crown Prince and Mary."

"I love Mary as a sister," the Countess said quietly. "It seems rather strange to learn that she is indeed my cousin."

As the carriage passed over the cobblestone streets of Vienna, the two ladies embraced within an ambience of truth and understanding for the first time.

"I promise," the Countess whispered, "to take care of Mary Vetsera and her baby in America, Baroness. I will not forsake them."

SIX

MOONLIGHT CREATED EERIE SHADOWS AMONG THE TREES AS A lone carriage squeaked over the snow, lacing its way to the outer perimeter of the city of Vienna. Countess Larisch tried to absorb every detail of the beauty around her, and thus cast the fear from her heart. But the time for rendezvous was drawing near, and her hand trembled as she smoothed the folds in her long skirt.

Suddenly she heard voices and the movement of restless horses. As her carriage came to a stop, the driver opened the door. She quickly stepped down and looked around. Baroness Vetsera and Agnes were walking toward her.

"Quickly," the Baroness whispered. "Get into the royal carriage."

The Countess followed the two ladies to the coach and silently stepped inside. Empress Elizabeth gave her a glance of acknowledgment as she crowded in among the three passengers and their belongings. The carriage jerked as the driver snapped the reins on the rumps of the team. With guardsmen posted both fore and aft, the carriage slowly wound through the shadows of darkness along the narrow roads en route to the train station in Badan. Everyone in the coach was silent and immobile as though a word or a movement would shatter their veil of secrecy.

Suddenly Empress Elizabeth broke the stillness. Her voice was full of emotion.

"This whole thing is too unbelievable for words," she said softly. "My son is dead. Austria is dead. And I *feel* dead. I, the Empress of Austria and the Queen of Hungary, have had everything at my disposal. And now, I am leaving, fleeing like a thief in the night. But this thief is fleeing with nothing more than tarnished dignity and wishing only to retain sanity."

Again, Empress Elizabeth fell silent. No one responded to her utterance, nor did they look at her. Countess Larisch concentrated on the shadows dancing through the interior of the coach for the duration of the ride to the train station.

The rhythmic throb of the train engine echoed through the cold winter night as the ladies disembarked from the carriage. Countess Larisch stepped down onto the frozen snow and looked back toward the city of Vienna.

I am indeed going to miss you and your aristocratic charm, dear Vienna, she thought. *But the opera, the arts, and your charismatic mode of living will remain a part of me forever.*

She turned and walked toward the station. A pillar of smoke drifted slowly upward from the engine, vanishing into the starlit heavens. As the Countess joined the entourage at the boarding platform, the engineer trumpeted the whistle for departure. The four women quickly boarded and settled into their compartment for the long journey to Trieste.

"We are one step closer to knowing the extent of Mary's injuries," Baroness Vetsera said quietly.

"Yes," Empress Elizabeth sighed. "And one step closer to obscurity."

For a time, the only sound within the compartment was the throbbing clatter of iron wheels against the rails and an occasional toot of the engine's whistle.

Countess Larisch looked at the Baroness. Her face was white, and her eyes had dark circles of exhaustion beneath them.

"My concern is for Mary. I am afraid of what I will find. Indeed, mental preparation for our final farewell will be the harshest moment of reality that I shall ever have to face."

"We must try to get some rest," the Countess advised. "The past forty-eight hours have taken a heavy toll on each one of us."

As the train surged forth through the night, the four ladies became lost in their private thoughts, uncertain of destiny and suppressing malevolent doubt. In a state of mental exhaustion, they left Austria and crossed a portion of Yugoslavia. Over seven hours later, the train braked to a halt at the station in Trieste, Italy.

"Wake up, Countess. We have arrived."

The voice of Agnes filtered through the maze of strange dreams, ultimately awakening awareness in the Countess.

She slowly sat up.

"Where are we?"

"Trieste, Countess. Please hurry," Baroness Vetsera softly replied. "A carriage is waiting to take us to the port."

"Yes, of course," she said.

The Countess quickly stood and brushed her hair back with one hand.

"Forgive me. I did not realize how fatigued I was . . ."

Empress Elizabeth raised her hand.

"You must not apologize, my niece. Your anxiety over Mary had peaked long before most were aware of an immediate problem. Perhaps you will be able to get some rest after we board the freighter."

Countess Larisch lowered her gaze in gratitude before hurriedly gathering her meager belongings. Then she followed the three ladies through the train car.

A cold gust of wind hit them as they stepped onto the platform in front of the station. The air was humid and heavy with the scent of the sea. A gentleman met them and bowed to the Empress.

"Your carriage awaits you, Empress. Follow me, please."

Baroness Vetsera, Agnes, and Countess Larisch exchanged fearful glances. But Empress Elizabeth remained composed as she followed the man. He helped them into the coach before returning to the station for their luggage.

The Empress looked at each frightened face and calmly said, "I am on yet another frivolous vacation, Ladies. Please remember that. Everything is going according to schedule."

Agnes and Countess Larisch looked at one another. A faint smile of relief surfaced on both of their faces. Countess Larisch settled back against the seat and closed her eyes.

"I am grateful for our safe journey thus far, but I am not looking forward to the voyage," Agnes said quietly.

"I, too, am dreading the long journey across the water," Countess Larisch murmured. "The weather does not seem the best for a pleasant voyage."

The carriage soon started forward and slowly moved through the streets of Trieste. Countess Larisch peaked around the drape to catch a fleeting glimpse of the bustling city by the sea. The town was a flurry of activity. Women were walking along the street firmly clutching their parasols against the gusty wind. Italian businessmen hustled about, engrossed in their daily ventures, and a dozens of horse-drawn carriages rambled along the busy thoroughfare. Thus the modest carriage accommodating the secretive band of Austrian nobility passed unnoticed.

Countess Larisch released her hold on the drape and positioned her body more comfortably.

Perhaps there is life after Vienna, she mused. Agnes seemed to read her thoughts and smiled at the Countess.

Suddenly Baroness Vetsera cleared her throat and moved to the edge of the seat.

"There is something I must tell you," she said. "Now! Before it is too late."

The statement was so abrupt that Empress Elizabeth, Countess Larisch, and Agnes looked at her without responding.

The Baroness took a deep breath and slowly exhaled. She looked at Empress Elizabeth before quietly saying,

"Mary's father, Baron Johann Albin Vetsera, is alive."

Icy silence was broken by the Empress a moment later.

"Johann?" she whispered. "Johann is alive?"

"Yes, Your Highness," the Baroness replied. "He is living in America. Eight years ago, he was reported dead. His death was attributed to a heart attack while in Cairo on business. In truth, Emperor Franz Josef had him excommunicated from Austria after learning of the misbegotten child he had sired. Even I was not informed of the deception until an Austrian diplomat came forth with the truth."

"Go on," the Empress implored. "Please share the details for Mary's sake."

Although her lips trembled, the tale of falsehood was precise and clearly orated by Baroness Vetsera.

"The diplomat who came forward helped Johann escape and described his final hours before deportation. He is indeed living in America and has changed his name to John Vecera."

As the Baroness paused for a moment, Empress Elizabeth drew a deep breath and leaned back.

"Why do you tell us this now?" she asked quietly.

"Johann loved Mary very much," the Baroness said softly. "And, if you can find him, I pray that he will make your lives in America both safe and happy. He is a horse trader in a small German and Czech settlement called LaGrange, Texas."

"Thank you, Baroness Vetsera," Empress Elizabeth said happily. "I am grateful that you shared this information. It may be invaluable."

A faint smile was evident as the Baroness said, "I wish only health and happiness for the four of you. Perhaps I have been able to ease a bit of the fear and pain of exile."

With these words spoken, the travelers were silent. The rhythmic beat of the horse's hooves on the road seemed soothing to Countess Larisch. She placed her head against the drape and closed her eyes.

Moments later, the sound of water lapping against the shoreline and men shouting to one another induced her to open her eyes and peak through the window. The carriage was approaching the docks at the Port of Trieste. She felt her heartbeat quicken as the bow of the freighter came into view. The vessel was a dull gray in color with random streaks of rust across the beam. The lone smokestack was painted white with a thin line of black at the rim. It indeed had the appearance of a trustworthy, old mariner, weathered and wise to the many moods of the sea. A flag was flying above the bridge where the captain now stood, issuing orders to the men on the deck below. Crates and barrels of cargo lined the dock, waiting to be winched aboard and stowed by the crew. The Countess closed the drape and bowed her head.

Stowaways en route to a new land, she thought. *How devastating!*

As the carriage came to a halt near the loading dock, she quietly moved forward and said, "This is our blessed passage to safety. May it carry us swiftly and safely to begin life anew."

Murmurs of agreement echoed within the coach as the door suddenly swung open.

SEVEN

A STEADY BREEZE WAS BLOWING ACROSS THE GULF OF VENICE as Empress Elizabeth, Countess Larisch, Baroness Vetsera, and Agnes disembarked from the carriage. Baron Krauss met them at the gangplank.

"I am pleased that you arrived in good time," he said. "Mary is on board and resting comfortably in the infirmary. The ship's doctor is with her, which gives me the opportunity to brief you before boarding."

"Yes?" Empress Elizabeth asked. "Have all arrangements been confirmed?"

"Yes, Empress. Indeed they have."

Baron Krauss clasped his hands behind his back and began pacing in front of the four ladies.

"Gratuities have been paid to the Captain, and he and the ship's doctor have taken a vow of silence."

Baron Krauss stopped pacing and stood in front of Empress Elizabeth.

"The freighter is charted to dock in the Gulf of Mexico at Port Galveston. Galveston is a major seaport on the coast of Texas."

Countess Larisch glanced at Baroness Vetsera, but the matron did not flinch as Baron Krauss continued.

"Your vows of silence remain with you throughout the voyage and beyond," he said firmly. He looked at each lady before adding, "That is all. Have a safe voyage."

As he departed their company, Countess Larisch and Agnes glanced at one another.

"Galveston," Agnes whispered. "Galveston, Texas!"

Empress Elizabeth and Baroness Vetsera shot warning glances at the maid before following the Captain on board the ship. Countess Larisch patted her on the shoulder and fell in step behind Baroness Vetsera.

Each lady was assigned a stateroom, none more impressive than the other. Each contained a single berth and a wash stand with a small mirror above it.

"Stow your belongings under the berth," the Captain explained. "If we hit rough seas, everything needs to be as secure as possible."

After the Captain ushered Empress Elizabeth, Countess Larisch, and Agnes to their separate staterooms, he turned to Baroness Vetsera.

"Follow me, please."

Countess Larisch quickly stowed her belongings beneath the bunk. She dampened a cloth and cleaned the road dust from her face and hands and combed her hair.

I will check on Empress Elizabeth before going to the infirmary, she decided. *Perhaps Baroness Vetsera and Mary need time alone anyway.*

The Empress did not answer when the Countess tapped lightly on the door. After a moment, Countess Larisch opened it a crack and saw the Empress sitting on the berth, expressionless and eyes vacant as though in a trance.

"Your Highness, are you all right?" she quietly asked.

The Empress did not move nor answer. Countess Larisch sat down beside her and began talking in a slow, soothing voice.

"Everything will be all right," she said. "We have made connections thus far without any problems. And very soon you, Mary, Agnes, and I will arrive safely in America."

Empress Elizabeth still did not respond. The Countess gently lifted her chin and forced the Empress to look at her.

"Perhaps talking about it will help. Do you realize that we three: you, Baroness Vetsera, and I are very much alike?"

The Empress slowly shook her head. Countess Larisch stood up and gazed through the porthole above the berth.

"It is true. Our love for Mary was so protective and intense that we almost caused her demise."

The Countess turned back to face the Empress. She was now attentive and alert. The Countess gazed up and continued.

"You by protecting her from tarnished heritage, Baroness Vetsera by allowing an over-abundance of freedom to do as she pleased, and I by assisting, even encouraging, the love between her and the Crown Prince. And now, Empress Elizabeth, my dear, sweet aunt, we face the consequence of fallacy. We must be strong, savoring precious memories of days gone by and gaining wisdom from the aftermath of error.

"My love for Baroness Vetsera will never dim with the passage of time. I have shared many times of happiness with her and felt her pain during misfortune. I was at the opera with the Baroness the day that Ladislaus, her son, died in the fire at the opera house. I was also with the Baroness when she received word of Baron Vetsera's death in Cairo. Soon she will be leaving our lives forever, and I will be unable to offer solace."

Empress Elizabeth stood up and walked to the door. She opened it and turned to the Countess.

"You and I should get some fresh air and clear our heads of gloom before the ship leaves port. It is probable we will never see the shores of Europe again. But," she paused and smiled at the Countess. "Due to your words of understanding, I believe that I can now say farewell with dignity."

They slowly walked up the ladder to the deck. The cold sea breeze now felt good to the Countess. She and Empress

Elizabeth were lost in private thoughts as they leaned against the rail and gazed upon the mainland.

"You should return to your staterooms at once and remain there for the majority of the voyage."

The stern, deep voice of Baron Krauss frightened the two ladies, and they whirled around to face him.

"Your presence on this ship does not insure your safety. Other passengers or even some of the crew may have ulterior motives for being aboard this vessel. Meanwhile, all titles of nobility are hereby terminated. Safeguard the monarchy."

The Baron paused for a moment before raising his hand and adding, "God speed!"

He abruptly turned and walked across the deck to the gangplank. The two women silently watched him step inside the carriage and close the door before retracing their steps to the staterooms below deck.

Meanwhile, Baroness Vetsera had followed the Captain through the narrow passageway to the stern of the ship and to the infirmary. They quickly entered a small room to the starboard and closed the door.

"Doc," the Captain said, "this is Baroness Vetsera."

"Yes, I have been expecting her," the ship's doctor said quietly. "Thank you, Captain."

After the Captain closed the door, the doctor turned to the Baroness.

"Mary is in shock and weak from the loss of blood," he said quietly. "Don't allow her to get too tired."

Baroness Vetsera walked to the bunk and sat down on a chair near the slumbering patient. Mary's face looked pale and lifeless. A stained bandage covered the upper crown of her head; her long hair lay across the pillow, matted and discolored with dried blood. Tears streamed down the matrons' face as she stared at the swollen discoloration around the eyes of her adopted daughter. She gently touched the girl on her shoulder and kissed her cheek. Mary slowly opened her swollen eyes and took sight of her mother's grieving face. She reached for her mother and they embraced lovingly.

"Be still, My Precious Child," the Baroness whispered. "Don't try to talk now. Just rest."

A faint smile appeared on the girl's face as she again closed her eyes. Baroness Vetsera bowed her head and wept.

"Mama, I am so sorry."

"No," the Baroness whispered hoarsely. "I am to blame. Right now I just want to enjoy seeing you alive"

Baroness Vetsera felt a firm hand on her shoulder.

"It is time for you to leave now," the doctor said. "Mary will rest easier after I administer more ladanum."

"No, no, the Baroness begged hysterically with her arms wrapped tightly around Mary. You cannot take her away. She needs me. I need her."

"Come, Baroness. It is time to go," Countess Larisch said in a soft but firm voice.

Baroness Vetsera looked up and saw the Countess standing at the door. She looked back at the sleeping girl and again kissed her. Mary stirred but did not open her eyes.

"I love you, Precious One," the Baroness whispered. "Never forget that I love you."

Baroness Vetsera stood up and walked to the door without looking back at the still form on the bed.

My dear friend Baroness Vetsera is heartbroken, the Countess thought as she and the Baroness walked through the passageway to exit the ship. *I don't care what Baron Krauss demanded. I am remaining by her side as long as possible.*

Countess Larisch put her arm around the shoulder of the matron, and the two of them walked down the gangplank together. It wasn't difficult for the Countess to deduce what she was thinking. Her high hopes and dreams to marry her daughter into royal blood where she belonged now could never be.

As they approached the waiting carriage, the Countess suddenly stopped and turned to the Baroness. The two ladies silently looked at one another as though etching an eternal portrait in their minds.

"Please forgive me, Baroness Vetsera," Countess Larisch whispered.

Tears streamed down her face as the Baroness gently touched her cheek before stepping into the coach. Not another word was then spoken.

There, in the solitude of her carriage, the Baroness, mother of Mary Vetsera, would now have time to sort things out and prepare herself for the formidable times ahead, returning to a home that would be desolate—void of laughter, and void of the beautiful soul who would never walk those floors again.

Moments later, the driver slapped the reins on the rumps of the horses, and the carriage moved away from the Port of Trieste. Countess Larisch watched the departing coach fade against the Italian countryside. A cold breeze rustled her skirt as she cast a farewell kiss to her lifelong friend.

"It must be heartbreaking, my dear Baroness, to relinquish all rights to the princess who can never be," she murmured softly.

The Countess then turned and gazed at the freighter nestled against the dock.

"And, Empress Elizabeth Hapsburg, Queen of Hungary, it must be frightening to relinquish all rights to royalty; titles that will no longer be."

Countess Larisch walked back up the gangplank. Her posture was straight and proud, and her face was radiant with stalwart determination.

"I now," she said, "relinquish all rights and vow obscurity as we enter the threshold of a new frontier."

EIGHT

THE CARGO WAS LOADED AND STOWED BELOW DECK BY NOON. From the bridge, the Captain gave orders to cast off, and the mates quickly untied the lines from the dock. The whistle sounded one long blast, and the freighter slowly moved away from the pier. The Captain set a course through the Gulf of Trieste and into the Gulf of Venice.

The movement of the vessel through the water was smooth, and Countess Larisch sat on the bunk in her stateroom, peering through the porthole. As the mainland of Italy gradually disappeared from view, she yawned and leaned against the pillow.

I must go see Mary, she thought as her body slowly relaxed.

"But," she declared. "I am so tired! Perhaps if I just rest for a moment, I will . . ."

Twenty minutes later, someone rapped lightly on the door of the stateroom. A second knock broke through the veil of slumber, and the Countess sat up. She looked around the small cabin, making a desperate attempt to regain her bearings.

"Countess," Agnes whispered. "Countess Larisch, are you there?"

The Countess stood up and quickly tried to smooth the wrinkles out of her dress.

"Yes, Agnes," she called. "Just a moment."

She rubbed her eyes and brushed her hair back with one hand before opening the door and stepping back for Agnes to enter.

"I did not mean to bother you, Countess," Agnes apologized. "I thought perhaps we should go to the infirmary and see about Mary?"

"Yes, my friend," she smiled. "I intended for us to do that immediately after getting underway. But unfortunately, I am guilty of falling asleep."

"Understandable," Agnes replied with a grin.

"Thank you," Countess Larisch said, "Lets go check on her now."

Moments later, the two women walked through the door of the infirmary. The doctor was seated at his desk, looking at newly acquired medical literature as they entered. He peered over his spectacles and acknowledged them with a nod.

"Good afternoon, Doctor. I am Countess Marie Larisch and this is Agnes, both friend and maid of the Vetsera family."

"Good afternoon, Ladies," the doctor said. "Yes, Countess, I am glad to see you again. Thank you for your help with Baroness Vetsera earlier."

He motioned toward the hospital bunk.

"Our patient is sleeping quietly at the present time. I am giving her ladanum to relieve the pain and to help her rest."

Agnes quietly walked over to the bunk and looked down at Mary. She put her palm over her mouth to stifle a sob and glanced at the Countess.

"Yes, I know," Countess Larisch acknowledged. "It is a shock to see our pretty Baroness in this condition, Agnes. But the swelling and bruises will fade with time."

She turned to the ship's physician.

"Am I correct on this, Doctor?"

"Yes," he replied. "The exterior damage will improve dramatically in a few days."

"What can we do to help?" the Countess asked.

"It would be beneficial if one of you stayed with her around the clock," he said. "My duties encompass every crew member and passenger on board, and there are times when I cannot be in the infirmary."

"I will take the first shift," Agnes quickly offered.

"That will be fine, Agnes," the Countess agreed. "I will be back to relieve you about midnight."

By dusk, the freighter had passed through the Gulf of Venice and entered the rougher waters of the Adriatic Sea. Countess Larisch carefully walked down the passageway to the stateroom of Empress Elizabeth and knocked on the door.

"Who is it?"

"Countess Larisch, Empress. Would you care to join me for dinner?"

Empress Elizabeth opened the door and motioned for her niece to enter. The matron's eyes were red, and she dabbed tears from her cheeks with a handkerchief.

The Countess entered the cabin and shut the door.

"Are you all right?" she asked quietly.

Empress Elizabeth sat down on the bunk very slowly, accepting the pain from rheumatism in her knees and patted the cot for her niece to join her.

"Yes, my dear niece," she sighed as the Countess sat down beside her.

"As a matter of fact, my tears are tears of relief."

The statement startled the Countess, but she did not respond.

"I speak the truth. I watched through the porthole as we left the Port of Trieste. When we were out of sight of the mainland, I felt like a bird released from a cage."

Empress Elizabeth stood up and inhaled deeply.

"I have not felt contentment like this for many years. Vienna was my cage, and I could do nothing but watch the embittered royalty take my children away."

Countess Larisch listened without interrupting.

"My dear niece, please try to understand. I am now free! The only consolation for the loss of Rudolph is my freedom. Do you understand, Countess Marie?"

Empress Elizabeth gently touched her on the chin and looked directly into her eyes.

"Do you understand?" she repeated quietly. "I would sacrifice my upcoming freedom for the return of my son, but that can never be. I grieve for him, but I celebrate this opportunity to soar in the freedom of a new realm. My loss of Austrian and Hungarian titles and stature mean nothing to me. Mary is my life now."

Countess Larisch nodded and stood up.

"Yes," she said quietly. "I do understand."

The niece and her aunt embraced and smiled at one another.

"Now, dear Countess Marie, did you mention something about dinner? I do believe that my appetite is increasing with each nautical mile that we travel!"

"Yes," Countess Larisch winked. "In fact, we have been invited to dine with the Captain. And perhaps we should enjoy this notable hospitality. I truly doubt that commoners in America are offered such exclusive rights."

Empress Elizabeth and Countess Larisch chuckled as they passed through the stateroom door and walked toward the Captain's dining room.

The voyage was calm, and Mary slept soundly as the ship sailed across the Adriatic Sea and entered the open waters of the Mediterranean Sea. Although the freighter twice pulled into port for additional cargo within that forty-eight hour period, Countess Larisch, Empress Elizabeth, and Agnes did not venture onto the upper deck.

Countess Larisch was in the infirmary and at Mary's bedside when the young Baroness finally awakened from a long sleep.

"How are you feeling, Mary?" Countess Larisch quietly asked.

"Much better," Mary murmured, after a much needed hug.

Countess Larisch glanced at the doctor, and he immediately retreated. The Countess rested her hand on Mary's as the girl slowly looked around the room.

"Where am I?" Mary asked as her gaze returned to the Countess. "It looks dark and dreary. Why am I here?"

"You are in a hospital, Mary," Countess Larisch replied softly. "This is the infirmary on a ship."

Mary nervously glanced about the room again.

"A ship?" she asked. "Where are we going? How did I get here?"

Countess Larisch patted her hand and smiled reassuringly.

"I will explain everything, Mary, but it is very important that you remain calm."

Mary nodded and asked, "But is brother on the ship? Where is Mother? Where is . . ."

Suddenly Agnes entered the room with a tray of food in her hands and a big smile on her face. Countess Larisch was thankful for the gracious interruption.

"Agnes! I am so grateful that you are here," Mary said.

Agnes put the tray down on a counter and gently hugged the girl.

"I have been beside you through many hours of sleep, Baroness. I am so happy to see you awake. How are you feeling?"

"Hungry," Mary smiled. "The food smells wonderful."

The Countess and Agnes helped the patient sit up, and then they propped pillows behind her. Agnes held the tray steady as Mary slowly consumed the nourishment.

"You really should congratulate Agnes, Mary," the Countess chuckled. "She has been on board ship for two days now and has not complained about the poorly trained housekeepers or shoddy kitchen help yet!"

Mary giggled.

"That is a record, Agnes," she grinned. "You are a bit critical of unaccustomed servants, you know."

"Eat your vegetables, Baroness Mary," Countess Larisch said in a lighthearted tone. "They will make you look pretty and step lively!"

"I think she is feeling better already," Agnes said with a smile. "At least she is feeling well enough to tease me again."

"This girl will never be so bad that she cannot put you in your place, Agnes," the Countess added with a wink.

Mary smiled and ate another bite of the meal before motioning for Agnes to take the tray.

The two ladies helped Mary lie back on the cot. Agnes arranged the pillow beneath her head as Countess Larisch gently washed her face and hands with a damp cloth.

"You have not answered my questions, Countess Marie."

The Countess felt her nerves grow taut. She folded the cloth and set it on the counter before sitting down on the chair next to the bunk.

"Where are we going?" Mary persisted, "And why?"

Countess Larisch held Mary's hand and gazed at her bruised and swollen face for a moment.

"We are on board a ship en route to America," she said quietly. "We have left Austria due to the death that occurred at Mayerling."

"Rudi?" Mary whispered. "Rudi . . ."

Countess Larisch put her finger on Mary's quivering lips.

"Yes, Mary. Your Crown Prince is dead. That is why we must leave Vienna. Our dear Rudolph would not want us to be in danger or living a life of gloom."

"I recall it all too clearly," Mary finally said.

The Countess watched the expression on Mary's face. *Traumatic amnesia is not evident,* she silently noted. *As a matter of fact, Mary seems one step ahead.*

"Upon my arrival at Mayerling, Rudi was shocked. He asked me why I was there."

The infirmary suddenly felt cold and foreboding to the Countess. She shivered.

"Yes? Go on, Mary," she quietly urged.

Mary's voice sounded hollow, drained of life, as she continued.

"'Didn't you send for me?' I asked him."

The Baroness suddenly groaned as she touched the bandage on her head.

"Then I heard gunfire. Several shots were fired, and then, and then . . ."

"Shhh," the Countess interrupted. "Don't think about it for a while."

She patted the girl's face with a damp cloth, consoling her with warm words of reassurance. "I am with you now, and everything will be all right. Just rest now, Mary."

Countess Larisch laid the cloth across the eyes of the young Baroness.

As Mary's taut body relaxed on the bunk, Countess Larisch and Agnes exchanged a brief glance and breathed a sigh of relief. But the comfortable silence was soon shattered.

"My head hurts," Mary suddenly declared. "What happened to me?"

She put her hands on her head and traced the bandages with her fingertips.

"What is on my head?"

"A bullet grazed your head, Mary," the Countess gently explained.

Mary struggled to sit up. But nausea and dizziness overpowered her, and she fell back on the cot.

"Is Mother here?" she asked again in her delirium. "Why are we on a ship? Where are we going? Why are we leaving Austria? Oh, I don't feel well. My head hurts."

"We will talk more later, Mary," Countess Larisch said quietly.

"No!" Mary said angrily. "I am in pain and do not know why. I want answers. Now!"

"Please, Mary, lie still," the Countess pleaded. "You are going to injure yourself further."

Mary thrashed back and forth on the bunk, groaning and mumbling.

"Rudi. Oh, where is my Rudi?"

Suddenly her eyes widened with terror. Countess Larisch hugged the terrified girl in her arms and silenced her.

"You are with me now, Dear One. No one is going to hurt you."

"I remember!" Mary screamed. "Blood! There is blood everywhere. Rudi is . . . My Rudi's head. . . He is dead! My Rudi is dead!"

She suddenly fell silent. Her body went limp, and her eyes stared vacantly into space. Countess Larisch gently eased her head back onto the pillow. A moment later, Mary pulled the sheet over her head, and sobs of mourning echoed against the bleak and dreary walls of the ship's infirmary.

NINE

Countess Larisch slept restlessly that night. Visions of Rudolph raged within her as she tossed and turned on the small bunk. Time and again, she saw his body on the ground, showered with blood. Amid the shadows of darkness, Mary's terrified screams ripped through her subconscious, and she awoke many times, trembling and damp with perspiration.

At dawn, the Countess opened her eyes and looked around the stateroom. Gratitude for the new day suddenly brought a faint smile to her lips.

Sleep was not kind to me, she thought as she crawled from the bed and looked at the dark circles beneath her eyes. She hurriedly dressed and left the stateroom.

"I hope Mary was able to rest last night," she muttered as she walked down the passageway toward the infirmary. "Sleep will certainly assist in her healing process."

As the Countess entered the room, Mary raised her arms. Countess Larisch hurried to the bedside and embraced the girl.

"Please forgive my outburst yesterday," Mary said.

Countess Larisch lifted Mary's chin with her finger, gazing into her eyes.

"You should not apologize. I only wish that I could take away your pain."

The Countess dampened a clean cloth and gently wiped the girl's face and hands.

"Please tell me everything that has happened, Countess. My memory is deceiving. I cannot seem to recall what you told me yesterday."

The Countess sat down on the chair beside the bunk. With carefully chosen diction, she repeated the saga. Her voice was soft and reassuring, and Mary listened intensely to each detail. Ultimately, Countess Larisch inhaled deeply and leaned back in her chair. Mary did not comment nor ask further questions about the incident. For a short time, the distant throb of the steam engines and the occasional creak of the ship underway were the only sounds in the room.

Finally, Mary looked at the Countess and said with a raspy, inquisitive voice, "A lady dressed in black opens the door and peers at me quite often. She wears a black veil over her face, Countess. Do you know who she is?"

Countess Larisch hesitated a moment.

"Perhaps she is a relative of another patient," she said.

Mary accepted the explanation with a nod. A moment later, she put her hands on the head bandage and groaned.

"What is wrong," Countess Larisch asked.

She stood up and leaned over the girl, looking at the bandage for signs of fresh blood.

"Does your head hurt badly, Mary? I will get the doctor right away . . ."

With her hands still on the bandage, Mary wailed, "I must look dreadful!"

The unexpected outburst caused Countess Larisch to chuckle.

"You are feeling better, my friend," she gasped. "I am so pleased that your pride in physical appearance has remained intact."

A moment later, by chance, the ship's physician approached Mary's bed. He winked at Countess Larisch before looking down at his patient.

"Young Lady, it is time to replace your bandage. I believe we can replace it with a smaller one, don't you?"

Mary grinned and sat up on the side of the bed. The doctor removed the binding and cleaned the wound.

"You are very lucky, Mary," he said. "The bullet just grazed your head. There should be very little scarring from the injury."

"A scar?" Mary repeated loudly. "I am going to have a scar?"

Agnes quietly entered the room. She and Countess Larisch exchanged affirmative nods, but neither spoke. Words describing the patients condition were not necessary. Agnes could easily see the positive mental and physical change in Mary.

The doctor methodically bound the wound with fresh gauze before responding to Mary's outcry.

"Yes, my dear," he finally said. "A scar. A very small one, I might add. And your hair will easily conceal it."

After the doctor retreated from the bedside, Countess Larisch and Agnes brushed the girl's hair and applied blush to her pallid cheeks. After the cosmetic renovation, they stepped back to observe their efforts.

"Just a moment," the Countess said.

After applying a daub of perfume beneath each ear of the patient, she handed a mirror to Mary.

For one full minute, Baroness Vetsera stared at her reflection. Then, without warning, she threw the mirror on the floor.

"What am I doing? Why should I look nice now? Rudi is gone, and he was my reason for living! I wish that I had died too!" she screamed.

Countess Larisch grabbed Mary's shoulders and shook her.

"Stop it, Mary," she said hoarsely. "You are with child. Rudi's child! You must live."

"I do not want the baby," she retorted. "I want my Rudolph back!"

Countess Larisch sat down on the bed beside Mary. She took her hand and held it in her own.

"Mary, there is no greater gift a man can bestow upon his loved one. The child within you is Rudolph's gift of himself to you."

Mary picked up her pillow and held it in her arms. She rocked back and forth on the bunk, quietly sobbing.

Agnes shook her head and turned away. Countess Larisch watched in silence as the maid walked around the room, brushing the tears from her face.

"Please rest now, Mary," Countess Larisch said quietly. "I will ask the doctor to give you something to relax you."

As the Countess stood up, Mary reclined on the cot with the pillow still clutched in her arms. Many moans of heartache veiled the hospital room in a cloak of sorrow.

The following morning, Mary greeted Countess Larisch and Agnes with a wave and a smile. The Countess noted that her friend was sitting upright on the cot with her hair brushed and her eyes glistening with renewed life.

"Come in," Mary said. "I was hoping that you would come to see me early this morning. Let's have tea."

"That is a fine idea," Countess Larisch agreed. "Agnes, will you please gather the essentials for this engagement with our Baroness?"

"With pleasure," Agnes smiled.

As the maid scurried away, Countess Larisch walked toward Mary. But she stopped as Mary looked beyond her toward the door and gasped. The Countess followed her gaze to the figure now standing in the doorway.

Empress Elizabeth had entered the room. She was dressed in black, and her face was partially concealed behind a veil. Countess Larisch stepped aside as the matron slowly advanced toward Mary. She lifted her veil and smiled at Mary.

"Empress Elizabeth! But, but . . . " Mary stammered.

"Yes, Mary," the Empress smiled. "May I join you and Countess Larisch with a cup of tea?"

While Agnes tried to locate tea service befitting royalty, Empress Elizabeth sat down on the chair next to the bed.

"I do not understand," Mary said. "My life is like a dream. Your Highness, why are you here? Is Rudi with you?"

"No, my dear," the Empress replied. "You must face the truth. Rudolph is dead. He will no longer be a part of our lives."

"Aren't you angry with me?" Mary asked softly.

Empress Elizabeth shook her head slowly and stood up. She then embraced Mary.

"We will talk later, my child," she whispered. "Yes, indeed, we must talk later, and then you will understand. But," she hesitated. "But not right now."

Twenty-four hours later, Countess Larisch again walked down the passageway toward the infirmary. Her mood was one of optimism. The previous day had been uplifting and pleasant for everyone, which served as a healing elixir for Mary. However, as the Countess opened the door and stepped into the infirmary, she found the room in turmoil. Mary was in obvious agony, thrashing about on the cot and soaked with perspiration. Agnes fought the writhing body, desperately trying to soothe the patient with wet towels.

"What happened?" Countess Larisch demanded. "Why did you not call me?"

"I was afraid to leave her," Agnes replied. "Mary has a high fever. She put in a very bad night. The doctor said that the wound has become infected."

Countess Larisch noted that Agnes was on the verge of exhaustion. She touched her on her cheek. "It is time for you to get some rest, my friend. I will take over for a while."

Tears streamed down Agnes's face as she stepped back from the thrashing patient.

"The doctor said that this condition is serious," she sobbed.

Countess Larisch ignored the last statement. She gently patted the maid on the shoulder.

"You go now. Get some rest. I will take care of Mary."

As Agnes turned to leave, Countess Larisch grabbed the towels and began to bath the feverish patient.

Several hours passed before the fever subsided, and Mary was once again lucid. Countess Larisch sat down on the chair beside the bed. Although her body trembled with fatigue, she was grateful as Mary began to question prior happenings.

The Countess quietly filled in some of the voids that had previously been withheld from the Baroness. Mary listened as the bizarre story of treachery unfolded, exposing a clear view of the assassination of a son by his father.

"But," she exclaimed loudly, "it is not our fault. None of it is our fault!"

"Emperor Franz Josef felt that it was imperative for Rudolph to die," Countess Larisch said. "You do see that, don't you, Mary? But, I now fear that history may forever blame you for the death of the Crown Prince, rather than a martyr in a lover's suicide pact. I fear that Mary Alexandrine Vetsera will be considered a traitor, used as justification for the fall of the Hapsburg dynasty."

Mary stared straight ahead, accepting the information without comment. The Countess looked nervously at the girl, fearful that she had spoken too harsh in regard to the aftermath of rumor.

Suddenly Mary sighed and leaned back against the pillow.

"Rudi once told me," she said quietly, "that he was under constant surveillance by the monarchy. Although he was aware of the spies, he expressed intense apprehension over this last hunting trip to Mayerling. I did not understand his anxiety."

She hesitated a moment before adding, "After all, the outing was to be with his friend Count Hoyos and his brother-in-law

Count Phillip of Coburg. It sounded like a fun time of hunting. I could not comprehend his reasoning."

"Yes," the Countess murmured. "He spoke of his misgiving to me also."

"My Rudi had a strong conviction to, one day, be a great ruler in both Hungary and Austria. He often grieved over the adverse relationship with his father. My Rudi was concerned for his people and country, but he was never able to convince his father of that fact."

"It seems, Mary," the Countess interjected. "this tragedy within the House of Hapsburg will forever remain a part of all of us."

The Countess paused and looked at Mary. "Many years ago, my aunt Elizabeth accepted my illegitimate birth without question. Our love for one another goes beyond the germane love for a relative. Indeed, she is my friend. And my love for Rudolph and Vienna is much the same. It will remain with me forever, Mary, just as it will remain with you."

The Countess rested her hand on Mary's shoulder and continued, "But we must now embark on a new journey with hope and dreams for the future."

Mary drifted into a peaceful slumber as the ship slowly sailed toward the Strait of Gibraltar. Although shadowed in secrets from the past, the exiled nobility on board the freighter knew they had to survive the pain of error. The horizon beyond held their destiny, a promise of new life after treachery, deceit, and betrayal.

TEN

THE AIR FELT COOL AND REFRESHING AS COUNTESS LARISCH and Empress Elizabeth stepped on the deck of the ship. The Countess saw the captain standing by the ladder of the bridge. She waved and smiled at him.

The Captain tipped his cap in greeting as the women approached.

"Good afternoon, Ladies. It is good to see you topside."

"Thank you, Captain," Empress Elizabeth replied. "It feels wonderful. After nine days below deck, I am no longer concerned with Baron Krauss or his foreboding advise. I am more concerned with retaining good health and sanity."

The Captain chuckled and nodded in agreement. Countess Larisch stepped to the port railing and studied the southwestern horizon. A huge mass of dark clouds were forming above the expanse of Atlantic waters. The constant volley of lightening weaved long, luminous threads through the menacing formation, exposing the power suppressed within Mother Nature.

Countess Larisch felt uneasy as she noted the calm surface of the oceanic water and the lack of air movement. Her brow was creased with worry as she turned to face the Captain and Empress Elizabeth.

"Captain, a severe storm appears to be developing."

Empress Elizabeth patted her on the arm and said, "My dear niece, you have been below deck too long. After assisting

Mary through days of delirium, I can readily sympathize with your low tolerance of optimism. However," she said as she glanced at the Captain, "a storm at sea is rather invigorating. Don't you agree, Captain?"

He smiled and shook his head, "Well, I am afraid that I never thought of it as invigorating."

"I have travelled a great deal, and I have found that storms at sea are comparable to a strange dog. Their appearance is far worse than their bite."

Countess Larisch and the Captain laughed as the matron continued.

"The wind from a storm at sea breaths new life into my soul."

With a wave of her hand, the Empress dismissed the officer as though he was a servant.

"Carry on, Captain. My niece will learn to accept and enjoy the many moods of the ocean."

Countess Larisch and the Captain exchanged knowing glances, and the Captain bowed.

"Yes, Empress."

He bowed to the Countess and stepped up the ladder to the bridge.

Thirty minutes later, the two women descended the ladder to the lower deck. The fresh air had revived their optimism, and a healthy color had returned to their cheeks. However, the mood was somber as they entered the infirmary. The doctor diverted them from approaching Mary's bunk, motioning for them to follow him instead. He took them back out into the passageway. As the door closed behind them, the doctor spoke with resignation.

"Empress Elizabeth," he said quietly, "I am afraid that Mary's condition has become critical."

Countess Larisch saw the matron waver from the impact of the report and put her arm around her shoulders for support.

"I am sorry," the doctor continued, "but Mary's fever is now so high that I fear she will lose the baby. I have given her large doses of quinine to lower her temperature, but the treatment has been to no avail. Mary and her child are now in God's hands. There is nothing more that I can do. . ."

"Please, Doctor," Empress Elizabeth interrupted. "Give her more quinine. I feel the medication will decrease the rampant fever and increase her and the baby's chance for survival."

"No, Madam!" he declared loudly. "The risk of severe damage or death from the misuse of this drug is far too great. I will not administer additional quinine!"

He walked back into the hospital room and closed the door.

Suddenly Empress Elizabeth turned around and briskly walked down the passageway toward the ladder. Countess Larisch followed as the matron stepped onto the upper deck. The wind from the approaching storm had hit, and the Empress grabbed the rail to steady herself.

"Mary and the grandchild are my salvation from the living dead," she said. "The baby will grant me comfort and companionship in the strange land. Boy or girl, the child is all that remains of my son."

Countess Larisch reached for the Empress, but a wave smashed against the beam of the ship, forcing her to grasp the rail with both hands.

"We must go below, Empress!" she shouted above the howl of the wind. "The storm is growing more intense by the second. It is dangerous to stay on deck!"

Countess Larisch looked at the Empress and frowned. The face of the woman was pale and etched in a grimace of pain. "Oh, my dear aunt," she muttered. "The weather has caused your rheumatism to . . ."

"Go below!" a mate shouted. "Hurry! If you fall overboard no one can save you!"

The Countess tried to locate the spokesman amid the chaos on the deck, but the visual search spawned nothing more than panic.

"I need help!" she screamed. "My aunt is not able to walk! Please help us!"

Fifteen foot seas rammed against the beam of the freighter, and gale force winds pounded the two women who were clinging to the rail.

"Help! Someone please help us!"

A moment later, Countess Larisch saw a male passenger working his way across the pitching deck toward them.

"Let me help you," he shouted. "Hold on the rail with one hand and my shoulder with the other!"

Countess Larisch grabbed Empress Elizabeth's left hand and put it on the gentleman's shoulder. Then she put her body against the matron to stabilize her. The three slowly inched their way toward the ladder.

"Thank you," the Countess gasped as they descended into the lower deck.

Although the ship continued to roll and pitch with each breaker, the motion was less intense along the ballast. The roar of the wind topside ebbed with distance as they walked through the passageway, clutching the grab rail.

"Yes," responded Empress Elizabeth. "Thank you. We were in a desperate situation."

"I am glad to be of service," he responded. "The storm caught me off guard also."

As the gentleman opened the door for Empress Elizabeth to enter her stateroom, he asked, "May I be of further assistance?"

Empress Elizabeth touched his shoulder and gazed into his eyes.

"Yes," she whispered with a slightly upturned lip. The Empress made a tiny, almost undetectable gesture of one hand and mouthed the word "Quinine."

"Pardon me, Madam," he responded softly. "Did you say 'quinine?'"

"My daughter and her unborn child are in the ship's infirmary in critical condition. While the tempest rages above, Mary is fighting her own storm," the matron said. "The doctor has refused to administer additional quinine to reduce the fever. I feel that he is making a mistake. Perhaps a fatal one."

The man gazed at Empress Elizabeth and Countess Larisch for a moment. Then he slowly nodded his head and replied, "Yes. I have quinine in my stateroom, Madam. The medication was for my wife. But she is now deceased, and I have no further need for it."

Before either lady could respond, the gentleman left the stateroom.

"Do you feel it is wise to go against the doctor's orders?" Countess Larisch whispered.

"Yes, in this instance, I do," Empress Elizabeth said in a strong, firm voice. "Quinine is their only hope. I have nothing to lose and everything to gain by proceeding with the medication."

"Yes," the Countess agreed. "I understand your judgment."

After a light knock on the door, the gentleman again entered the stateroom. He handed Empress Elizabeth a handkerchief.

She quickly untied the small bundle. The fabric fell away from the center, exposing a minute amount of yellow powder. The Empress stared at it for a moment before glancing up to thank the donor, but he had already left the stateroom. She quickly secured the bundle and placed it in her footlocker.

The ship suddenly creaked and lurched as another wave engulfed the deck. After helping the matron settle onto her bunk, Countess Larisch sat down beside her.

"I want you to stay here, Aunt Elizabeth, while I go get Agnes. She must be terribly frightened. The storm seems to be increasing, and one should not endure its wrath alone."

"Yes," the Empress replied. "I . . ."

A bolt of lightening struck near the ship, and a scream was lost amid the deafening clap of thunder that followed in its wake. The freighter jerked violently as another enormous wave pounded against her beam.

"Go now," the Empress said. "But be careful and hurry back."

"Yes, I will."

Countess Larisch closed the door behind her and slowly inched down the unsteady passageway. As the ship reeled from another waft of water, the Countess lost her grip on the grab rail and fell.

Meanwhile, the crew members went down the hallway passing out towels and sheets, giving instructions on how to use them for protection.

"Tear the sheets into strips and tie down all moveable objects and furniture to larger, more stable pieces," they said. "Wrap the towels around babies and the heads of older children."

They went on to explain that the elderly as well as the sick would have to be tied down to their beds. Many were paralyzed with fear. Most of them had never traveled by seas before and were petrified of the water. Everyone willing obeyed orders. The howling wind and pounding rain quieted the people as they listened intently. The only human sounds came every so often when there was a chuckle out of the children. They thought it fun to reach out for smaller objects that kept sliding their way as the ship rocked more fiercely. Screams and cries from the young on board echoed against the howl of the wind and the creaking protests of the vessel as the Countess crawled toward Agnes's stateroom.

"Agnes, open the door!" she yelled as she pulled herself upright beside the cabin. She found the latch and quickly entered the room. Agnes was laying on her bunk. Her legs were curled up tight to her chest, and her eyes were closed.

"Agnes," Countess Larisch shouted above the storm. "Are you all right? Come with me to the stateroom of Empress Elizabeth. We will weather the storm together."

Agnes did not move or open her eyes.

"Please, Agnes," the Countess pleaded. "The storm will pass, but right now the Empress needs us. Please, Agnes. Get up!" she screamed.

The maid opened her eyes and sat up. She followed as Countess Larisch stumbled back through the door and entered the swaying passageway.

"Go to your staterooms!" a ship's mate yelled.

His countless hours aboard ship were evident as he ran down the passageway toward them.

"Where are you going?" he yelled.

"To the first stateroom," Countess Larisch replied loudly. "Will you help us?"

He steadied the two ladies as they slowly moved down the grab rail.

"The Captain is in beam sea right now, but he is trying to set a heading into the storm."

Another bolt of lightening streaked through the darkened sky and smashed against the water's surface. Countess Larisch closed her eyes to suppress the glare and waited for the deafening roar of thunder. Within two seconds, the sound bellowed through the ship, vibrating her every fiber with resonant and horrifying force.

The Countess wished desperately for this nightmare to end. She felt as though she was in hell itself. *How else*, she thought, *could anyone describe such a horrid scene?*

"Is everything stowed and secure in your cabin?" the mate shouted as they approached the Empress's stateroom.

"Yes," Countess Larisch countered in a loud voice.

"Then stay in this room until the storm has subsided," he ordered. "You are on a seaworthy vessel. She will take care of you, if you help take care of yourself!"

Countess Larisch and Agnes stumbled into the stateroom and closed the door. Empress Elizabeth was lying down, clutching the sides of the bunk with her eyes wide open.

Countess Larisch fell to her knees and crawled to her side.

"Are you all right, Your Highness? Is there anything I can do for you?"

The Empress shook her head. Countess Larisch and Agnes reclined on the floor beside the bunk.

The three, bound by exile, were now cast within a watery nightmare. Darkness, fear, and illness were their sole companions as the storm vented its wrath upon the sea.

Meanwhile, many of the other passengers prayed—some silently—some verbally. Soon the praying turned to screams as the swell was now upon them. The ship rose slowly, then it bashed down against the waves. Both the passengers and crew were buffeted in every direction. There were screeching noises almost unbearable to the ear, as if the ship was breaking apart. Other sounds of even greater intensity followed that undoubtedly instilled fear in the bravest. As the severe motions continued, sea sickness began to take its toll. Some became deathly ill and threw up right where they were. A ghastly stench filled the air. No one spoke; only moans came from the elderly, and cries from the babies and children.

Alone and defenseless, the ship rode the massive swells of the Atlantic waters, plummeting downward as the surface disappeared from beneath her hull. But, each time, she gallantly rose from the depths to face the adversary with renewed courage.

ELEVEN

COUNTESS LARISCH WOKE UP AND LOOKED AROUND THE STATE-room. Agnes was no longer beside her, and Empress Elizabeth was sleeping on her bunk. The violence of nature had passed, and now the bilge pumps were removing the access water from the hull with a monotonous throb. A faint smile appeared on the lips of Countess Larisch as she observed the ray of sunlight that was streaming through the porthole. The gentle sway of the ship's movement through the water felt comforting and secure.

Thank You, God, the Countess silently prayed. *Thank You for granting us this new day.*

She slipped over to the footlocker and quietly retracted the bundle of quinine. She closed the lid and glanced at Empress Elizabeth, but the matron had not moved. As she opened the door of the stateroom, the stench of vomit permeated the lower deck. She cupped her hand over her nose and hurried down the passageway. The ship was quiet except for an occasional creak of the vessel or a shouted order from an officer.

Apparently exhaustion from fear and illness has suspended the usual bustle of early morning activity, she reasoned.

The doctor and Captain were standing outside the door of the hospital quarters, talking quietly.

"Good morning," Countess Larisch said as she approached.

"Good morning, Countess," the Captain responded. "You look reasonably fit after our stormy night at sea. How is Empress Elizabeth? I thought about her during the turbulence, but duty prevented me from personally checking on her."

"She is sleeping, Captain. Thank you for your concern, but I think we survived rather well. And the other passengers?" she asked.

"Everyone survived, although the clean up is going to be an enormous job," the Captain responded. "The doctor and I were just trying to coordinate ship damage with unsanitary health conditions. The dual responsibilities are going to require the cooperation of crew and passengers alike."

"Please advise us if we can be of assistance."

She turned to the doctor.

"How about Mary? Is she . . ."

The doctor patted her on the shoulder.

"Mary has had a rough night, Countess. I am afraid that motion sickness during the storm compounded her problem of high fever, infection, and pain."

Countess Larisch looked downward and said, "I should have been with her. I did not want to leave Empress Elizabeth alone."

"You did the right thing, Countess Larisch," the doctor replied. "The Vetsera maid spent most of the night with Mary. Due to the severity of the storm, we had to tie Mary on the bed. When the maid was overcome with exhaustion, she insisted on being tied next to the Baroness." He paused before adding, "Mary had outstanding care, considering the circumstances."

"Thank you, Doctor. I will see if I can relieve Agnes from her duty for a while."

The Countess gave a brief nod to each man and quickly slipped through the door of the infirmary. Agnes was changing Mary's sheets as she approached the bed.

"Oh my head," Mary cried. "My head hurts so much!"

The Countess noticed that her face was strained and pallid. Beads of perspiration across her nose and upper lip disclosed the presence of high fever.

Countess Larisch quietly joined Agnes at the bedside and whispered, "You go now and try to rest. I will stay with Mary."

Agnes glanced down at the patient and shook her head.

"No," she responded. "I will not leave her."

"Do as I say!" the Countess demanded. "You will be of no use to her if you get sick. Go now!"

Agnes sighed and slowly left the infirmary. The Countess finished changing the bedclothes and scrubbed the area. As she sat down on the chair next to the bed, delirium again emerged from the young Baroness.

For three hours, the Countess frantically bathed Mary in cold water and spoke gentle and loving words as she thrashed wildly on the cot. She smiled in gratitude as Empress Elizabeth and Agnes entered the infirmary.

"I am glad you are here," she breathlessly whispered. "I don't know what else to do. Her fever seems to be rising, but the cool cloths are not helping."

"I looked for the package in the footlocker," the Empress responded quietly, "but it was gone. Do you have it?"

"Yes," the Countess answered, "but I don't believe we should go against the doctor's orders."

"Get it. Now!" the Empress demanded.

Countess Larisch hesitated only a moment before retrieving the bundle from beneath the bunk.

"This quilt is suffocating me," Mary babbled. "It is my fault! I should not be at Mayerling. Not here! Not now! I am putting Rudi's life in jeopardy by being here!"

Countess Larisch and Agnes stood quietly as Empress Elizabeth embraced the irrational girl, but the gesture of security did not prevent Mary from reliving the nightmare.

"I only love Rudolph," she said as she gnashed her teeth. "I want Rudolph. How can I possibly take care of the baby without him?"

Empress Elizabeth gestured to Agnes, and the maid scurried across the room to prepare the medicinal solution.

Seconds later, the precious fluid passed between Mary's lips, and the prayers for a miracle commenced.

The following two days were spent in attendance of Mary. Empress Elizabeth, Countess Larisch, and Agnes rotated shifts, each one hoping to hear a positive report as she entered the infirmary for her interval.

On the morning of the third day, Agnes entered the room, and Countess Larisch slowly shook her head.

"Perhaps our Mary will show signs of recovery before too much longer," the Countess whispered.

"But it has been so long since she received . . ."

"Shhh," the Countess warned. "You must not lose faith."

She put her arm over the maid's shoulder and said, "None of us can afford to lose faith."

She slowly left the infirmary and walked toward her stateroom. Pausing beside the door, she gazed toward the ladder for a moment. *I do not recall the last breath of fresh air that I had*, she thought. *And* now *seems like the perfect time to grab one.*

Two minutes later, Countess Larisch walked across the deck and stood at the rail. She gazed across the calm Atlantic waters, trying to visualize the scene created during the storm. "Mother Nature can be so deceiving," she said to herself.

"You have certainly experienced the many moods of the sea during this voyage, haven't you, Countess Larisch?" the Captain chuckled.

The unexpected comment astonished the Countess, and she whirled around.

"My apologies, Madam," the Captain added. "I did not mean to startle you."

Countess Larisch smiled and replied, "No apology necessary, Captain. I was just thinking that our wounds heal much slower than those of the sea. The water is so benevolent, calm, and clear today, but several days ago, it was an angry adversary. Then I feared for my life, and now I admire its beauty."

The Captain clasped his hands behind his back. He gazed at the Countess without speaking, until she felt uncomfortable and nervously began to tap her fingers on the rail.

"Captain, is there something wrong?" she finally asked.

He lowered his gaze and shook his head. "Once again, Countess, please forgive me. Indeed, I do need to talk to you. I hesitate because you have enough worries, but my problem encompasses the entire ship."

"Yes?" she asked. "What is it?"

"We were blown off course during the storm," he said grimly. "I was unable to determine the gravity of our situation until the clouds dissipated about midnight last night. The celestial reading on my sexton indicates that we are now hundreds of miles due north of our charted course."

The Countess looked bewildered.

"What does that mean?"

"Our supplies, both water and food, are inadequate for the extended voyage."

"Are you saying that we should begin rationing, Captain?"

"Yes, Countess Larisch. Immediately." He paused a moment before adding, "The morale of the crew and passengers has been a bit low since the battering by the storm. I can handle the crew, but I would appreciate your help in dealing with the passengers."

She wondered what Baron Krauss would think *now* about his suggestion that she maintain a low profile. But it did not matter. This was an emergency.

"Of course, Captain."

The Captain quietly outlined the plan of allocation as they walked back across the deck.

The brow of Countess Larisch was creased with concern as she descended to the lower deck. She appreciated the faith that the Captain had shown in her, but she too felt nervous about the passengers acceptance of this latest crisis.

Moments later, in a calm and matter-of-fact voice, she relayed the message to the fared storm victims.

"We will be fine if we follow the guidelines set by the Captain," she concluded.

Although murmurs of protest echoed among the gathering, each passenger vowed to uphold the limited ration rule.

"I don't understand why the Captain didn't make allowance for additional supplies before we left the last port," one woman complained.

Countess Larisch smiled and said, "He had no way of knowing about a storm of this magnitude. And, we must remember that he kept us upright and afloat for many hours."

Again, she heard murmurs among her audience, but this time nods of agreement accompanied the comments.

"It is important that we maintain a healthy perspective and look forward to our safe docking at Port Galveston," she said. "If I can be of any assistance, please let me know."

She quickly turned and left the area without further adieu. Although fear and dread gripped her heart, she did not want to let others see her frailty.

Many days passed before the convictions of faith began to wane within the passengers aboard the ill-fated freighter. With rations limited to raw potatoes and a modest amount of water per day, despondency set in. Starvation and dehydration appeared imminent. Some even contemplated suicide. Day after day, eyes looked upon the watery horizon, straining to catch a glimpse of land, but the effort was wasted.

Thus, the calm after the storm became an epic tale of endurance, courage, and stamina. Indeed, a crippled vessel sustained her wounded, sailing ever southward through the tranquil Atlantic waters beneath a cloudless, azure sky.

TWELVE

"HER FEVER HAS BROKEN," THE DOCTOR SAID. "I BELIEVE Mary is a miracle. She is no longer in critical condition."

Countess Larisch looked at Empress Elizabeth. Relief and renewed hope glistened within the tired eyes of the Empress. *Your quinine*, the Countess thought. *You saved your daughter's life with quinine, Your Highness!*

"Your Mary has survived insurmountable odds," the doctor continued. "Go to her now. She is conscious and anxious to see you."

Agnes was brushing Mary's hair as the two women approached the bed. Although pale and thin, the patient had a faint blush of color on her cheeks and a smile on her lips. Agnes quickly arranged a portion of her dark hair across the healing wound on her forehead and straightened the lace on her pink gown.

Now was the chance Empress Elizabeth had been waiting for. Due to the storm's consequences she knew there was an all too strong possibility they would not survive. She could wait no longer to divulge her biggest secret to her daughter.

Countess Larisch pulled a chair up next to the cot for Empress Elizabeth, but the matron shook her head and sat down on the bed beside Mary. The Countess sat on the chair and waited in silence as the Empress moistened her parched lips. Then quietly and calmly she began to speak.

"Mary, I must reveal a truth that has been concealed from you since birth. I will now tell you why I am aboard ship with you."

Countess Larisch saw Mary's eyes widen with interest, but the young Baroness did not verbally respond.

"For many years, the whole of Europe watched and criticized me. They highly disapproved of me as queen, wife, and mother. Austria demanded that I remain by my husband's side, performing my official duties, but I was unable to conform to their expectations. Their constant condemnation held me in a state of bewilderment and depression, but on the other hand, Hungary appreciated me as I am."

Empress Elizabeth paused for a moment, glancing at Countess Larisch.

"I need a sip of water, Countess. Please," she said quietly.

Countess Larisch quickly handed a small ration of water to the matron. *Poor Aunt Elizabeth,* she thought as she returned to her chair. *This is not going to be easy for her.*

After sipping the precious fluid, the Empress resumed talking. Her voice was now strong and confident.

"When Emperor Franz Josef and I were married, we were truly devoted to one another. Our marriage was good for a time, but all too soon, aristocratic promiscuity tarnished our relationship. I was unable to accept his disloyalty and my loneliness."

Empress Elizabeth gently patted Mary's hand.

"I soon became bitter and angry with the rejection from my husband. Within his reign of the empire, there were countless mistresses, which cast me into the position of an Austrian figurehead. I no longer felt the love and compassion as a wife and mother. I grew to hate everyone in around me. I was temperamental and had a restless spirit. And, after months of despair, I began to travel. In the beginning, short excursions eased my pain, but soon my horizons broadened."

A faint smile appeared on the lips of Empress Elizabeth as she recalled her stolen moments as a carefree commoner.

"I felt a strong sense of belonging among the relaxed and friendly people. They gave me a new insight into life. The times I spent with them reminded me of the carefree days of my youth at Possenhoffen, my family's beloved home in the Bavarian Mountains."

Empress Elizabeth stood up and paced beside the bed a moment.

"With my new found freedom, I began to accept social invitations and made new friends, both male and female. Emperor Franz Josef, my children, and Austria became a distant and sorrowful obligation. I seldom returned home. And each time duty demanded my presence at the palace, the stay was short and worrisome. I returned to Hungary as quickly as possible, reclaiming my freedom and salving my bitterness with promiscuous affairs."

The Empress sat back down on the bed and looked at Mary.

"As you know, Mary, your father was Ambassador to Hungary and spent a great deal of time there, as did I." She paused.

Countess Larisch wondered if the Empress would be able to continue. Her face appeared ashen, and her body trembled as though under a tremendous strain. *Emotions are high,* the Countess silently pondered, *but starvation and dehydration are weakening her as well.*

A moment later, Countess Larisch was relieved to hear the matron continue. Again, her voice was strong and assured.

"Yes, Mary, one of my male friends was your father. You are the daughter of our time together. I am your mother, Mary. I am your true mother. Baroness Helene Vetsera and your father adopted you when you were merely days old."

The Countess glanced at Mary. The girl had not moved nor uttered a sound throughout the unveiling of her heritage.

Maybe she does not believe the Empress, Countess Larisch silently fretted. *But surely Mary wouldn't think the Empress was making up such a tale.*

Suddenly Mary put her hand on her face and tried to speak, but no sound came forth. Tears formed in her eyes and spilled down her cheeks, falling silently upon the pillow beneath her head.

Empress Elizabeth spoke soothingly as she brushed the dampness from her face.

"You see, my child, I am on this ship because I have wanted to retreat from Austria for many years. I am with you, and I now have a chance to be a part of your life in a new land. And soon, Mary, you will be giving me a grandchild; perhaps a grandson from Rudi. I love you so very much, my daughter, and I am truly proud of you."

Countess Larisch motioned for Agnes to follow her out of the infirmary. Before exiting, the Countess paused and looked back at the Empress and her princess. The two were embracing in acknowledgment of benevolent love. Countess Larisch sighed and smiled as she closed the door softly behind her.

In silence, Countess Larisch and Agnes walked down the passageway of the lower deck. They paused at the door of the stateroom and looked at one another.

"Lets go topside for a few minutes, Agnes," the Countess suggested. "A little fresh air would be good for both of us."

"Yes," Agnes agreed. "I was not looking forward to the isolation of my cabin."

Countess Larisch studied the maid's face for a moment. The trip thus far had been extremely hard on all of them. But Agnes had not rested for many days. And her eyes were now sunken and bordered with dark discoloration. The dramatic loss of weight and long hours of work without sleep had left her face lined and tired.

Countess Larisch rested her arm across Agnes's shoulder and smiled.

"It has been a long voyage, Agnes. Perhaps the ship will arrive in port soon, and we will fill our bodies with ample water and good, hot food. And," she added with a chuckle, "when that happens, our spirits will soar!"

The two ladies resumed walking toward the ladder.

"I am so relieved that Mary is aware of her birthright now," Agnes said as they stepped onto the deck.

"Yes," the Countess said. "The House of Hapsburg had lies and deceit hidden within the shadows for many years. It is healing for Empress Elizabeth to air the dank secrets." She gazed at the horizon for a moment before quietly adding, "Although, I am wondering if the world will ever know the truth behind the Mayerling tragedy."

"Land ho, Captain!" a mate suddenly shouted. "Off the starboard bow!"

"Land?" Agnes whispered. "Did he say land?"

"Yes, Agnes. Land! Water and food and solid ground beneath our feet again!" the Countess squealed.

As the ship sailed ever nearer to the land mass, crew members and passengers alike celebrated with shouts of gratitude and appreciation. Countess Larisch and Agnes stood at the rail with tears streaming down their faces as lines were thrown and tied to the pier. The Captain stepped onto the main deck from the bridge as the gangplank was lowered.

"All passengers are to remain on board while we take on provisions," he announced in a loud voice. "We have docked momentarily at Nassau, near the Andros Islands. I can assure you that the remainder of the voyage to Port Galveston will be far less dangerous and more comfortable. We will be underway within the hour."

Countess Larisch and Agnes stayed topside as crates and barrels were brought on board the freighter. Their eyes scanned the island, absorbing the green of the foliage and the brown of the dusty roads. The sight of solid ground filled their hearts with restored faith in reaching America to begin life anew. True to his word, within the hour the Captain strode up the gangplank.

Countess Larisch walked over to him and asked, "How long before we dock in Port Galveston, Captain?"

"I will be setting a course for the Gulf of Mexico," he replied. "We should easily reach port within sixty hours from now, Countess."

As he disappeared up the ladder to the bridge, the Countess turned to Agnes.

"Lets go below and tell the Empress and Mary. Perhaps we can take them some fresh water and fruit."

Moments later, one long blast from the ship's whistle sounded, and the freighter slowly moved through the harbor, taking a west by northwest heading toward the Strait of Florida.

The mood aboard ship that evening was one of heightening excitement and contentment for the careworn passengers and crew. As the moon drifted upward from the horizon, the soft strums from a mandolin laced the night air with lighthearted thoughts of tomorrow. And later that night, as those on board slept, the freighter from Trieste slowly entered the waters of the Gulf of Mexico.

THIRTEEN

FIFTY-SEVEN HOURS AFTER LEAVING THE DOCK IN NASSAU, THE freighter edged against the pier in Galveston, Texas. Lines were tossed to the port officials, and the Captain issued the order to cut the engines. Countess Larisch, Empress Elizabeth, and Agnes stood on deck beside Mary's cot with their forged passports in their hands. Although much improved, the Baroness was too weak to stand for any length of time. The four exiled women watched as wagons approached the pier and quickly began to load the European imports that were being lowered to the dock. Crew members, anxious for shore leave, hastened to lower the gangplank and to assist the other passengers onto the mainland. Although it was late winter, the air felt hot and humid, and Agnes held a cloth above Mary to shade her from the warm rays of the sun.

"I believe," the Empress suddenly said, "that the memory from this voyage will nullify any future thoughts of oceanic travel."

She glanced down at Mary and winked, and her daughter smiled.

"Why aren't we being taken ashore?" Mary asked.

Countess Larisch stooped down and whispered, "The Captain was ordered to hold us on board until the other passengers left the area for their hotels. Austria may be lurking in any corner to protect the monarch from disgrace, so we must keep a low profile."

"I understand," Mary sighed.

Finally, the foursome were escorted down the gangplank, and stepped onto solid ground for the first time since leaving Trieste, Italy.

"This feels wonderful," Countess Larisch stated as she stopped on the dock and looked around.

"It feels like the ground is moving," Agnes moaned. "I am getting seasick!"

Empress Elizabeth chuckled as she explained the phenomena to the pale and weak-kneed maid.

"That is normal after being on the water for so long. Sometimes the sensation does not leave me until the following day. But," she assured her companions, "you are not permanently damaged."

"I want to walk now," Mary said. "I will never regain my strength if I don't use my legs."

Countess Larisch and Agnes supported her as she stood up and looked around, finally resting her gaze on a river boat that was docked nearby. Men wearing big straw hats were rapidly loading the paddle-wheel vessel with big bales of cotton. The red, white, and blue flag of the United States of America waved proudly in the breeze above the bridge.

"America," Baroness Mary Vetsera murmured. "I cannot believe that I am standing on American soil and will never return to Austria."

"Nor can I," said Empress Elizabeth, as Countess Larisch and Agnes nodded in agreement.

"I am here to take you ladies to your quarters," a deep voice suddenly said.

All four women were startled by the sudden arrival of their driver. Countess Larisch bit her lip and silently scolded herself for not being more cautious. *We must learn to speak of Austria only in times of safe seclusion! Mary and her unborn babe are vulnerable to a second assassination for the sake of protecting Emperor Franz Josef's heir to the throne.*

She glanced at Empress Elizabeth, and the matron closed her eyes. The Countess felt as though she had read her thoughts.

Moments later, the women were seated in the modest, unadorned wagon. The heavy wheels creaked down the streets of Galveston, pulled by two large, dun-colored work horses. As they arrived in front of an old hotel, the driver pulled up the reins and halted the rig.

Countess Larisch gazed at the weather-beaten wood structure and sighed. *It certainly is not the exquisite and fashionable Grand Hotel in Vienna*, she thought, *but perhaps it will serve as a safe haven for us.*

The rugged-looking driver stepped down and assisted the four ladies from the wagon. He carried their luggage into the lobby and stacked it near the door.

"Have a good day, Ladies," he said as he doffed his hat.

After he left the hotel, Empress Elizabeth turned to Agnes. "You stay with Mary while the Countess and I make arrangements for our sleeping quarters."

The two women then slowly worked their way through the crowded and noisy room toward the registration desk.

"We need three rooms, please," Countess Larisch said, "for an indefinite period of time."

The clerk peered at the Countess over his spectacles and shook his head.

"I'm sorry, Ladies, but I only have two available right now. You are welcome to them," he cordially offered, "and we can make different arrangements later."

The Countess glanced at Empress Elizabeth. The matron had a stern expression on her face, but she nodded in agreement.

"That will do for now," the Countess responded. "We will take both available rooms, and you let us know when additional quarters become available."

The clerk handed the Countess two keys and motioned toward the stairs.

"Your rooms are up the stairs to your left. I will have someone carry up your belongings right away."

The Empress and the Countess turned and walked back through the boisterous crowd to Mary and Agnes.

"Mary, Agnes will be staying with you," the Empress said. "The hotel does not have adequate accommodations for the four of us, so Countess Larisch and I will share the second room."

Moments later, the Countess entered their room and looked around. The metal framed bed was covered by a red and slightly tattered quilt. The air had a faint scent of mildew, and the Countess quickly walked to the window and slid the pane up, allowing the sea breeze to cool and freshen the stale room.

Empress Elizabeth reclined on the bed and closed her eyes. Within seconds, Countess Larisch heard the heavy, deep breathing of slumber. She sat down on a chair near the open window and watched the bustle of activity below.

America is so different, she pondered. *There are no fine carriages, magnificent structures of stone, or displays of statuesque art. This will indeed be a challenge and a change for us.*

As dusk descended upon the Texas seaport, the Countess heard a faint knock on the door.

"Yes?" she asked quietly.

"It is I," Agnes immediately responded.

Countess Larisch quickly unlocked the door and bid Agnes to enter.

"The dining room is noisy and full of men. I thought you may prefer that I bring trays to your room."

Countess Larisch smiled and said, "Yes, Agnes, thank you. That would be very good."

"Mary has requested hot soup and tea again," the maid declared. "I will feel better when she is on solid food again."

"She will feel more like eating when she recovers from the voyage," the Countess assured her. "It feels so nice to have ground beneath us again. I believe all of our appetites will improve. Are you feeling better now, Agnes?"

"Yes, Madam, thank you," she grinned. "The world stopped tilting about two hours ago."

As the maid left the room, Empress Elizabeth sat up on the side of the bed. Countess Larisch lighted the oil lamp on the table and sat down. In the distance, she heard a piano and loud voices of men singing off-key. The music was lively and different than any she had heard before. She smiled and glanced at the Empress, but the matron seemed unaware of the unusual symphony.

Suddenly Empress Elizabeth stood up and walked to the window and peered down at the main street of Galveston Island.

"We must send a messenger to locate Baron . . . I mean," she stammered, "John. We are going to need his assistance in getting established."

Moments later, Countess Larisch left the room. The sound of laughter and loud voices drifted up from the dining area as she descended the stairs to the lobby. She went directly to the front desk and motioned for the clerk to assist her.

"I need a messenger immediately," she said. "He must be trustworthy, dependable, and swift."

The clerk leaned over the counter and looked at her, but he did not give any sign of understanding.

"I intend to pay him well for his services," she added.

"That makes a big difference," he said with a grin. "Yes, Ma'am, I know of a messenger. A mighty good one, too. I will get word to him right away."

"Fine. Send him up to our room as soon as possible."

As the Countess started back up the stairs, she suddenly stopped. "What are we doing?" she chidingly whispered. "Our Mary does not even know that her father is still alive, and we are sending word for him to come!" She ran up the stairs and quickly entered their chamber. Empress Elizabeth looked startled as she breathlessly shut the door behind her.

"What is wrong, my niece?" the matron asked. "Did the clerk question you about our request for a messenger?"

"No," she gasped. "No, he didn't. But, Empress Elizabeth, do you realize that Mary has not yet been informed of her father? His sudden and unexplained return into her life now would be like a ghost coming back from the dead. That child has been through so much already. We must tell her that her father did not die in Cairo!"

The lips of the Empress trembled as she pondered the best approach to the problem. She stood up and began to pace back and forth across the room. Moments later, she sat down and worked on her strategy.

"There is no easy way to expose the truth on this," she said. "We must tell her right away for he may soon be knocking at her door. We must tell her now."

Thirty minutes later, their fears over Mary's reaction were laid to rest.

"Papa?" Mary happily shouted as she absorbed the news. "Papa is alive?"

"Yes, my daughter," Empress Elizabeth said soothingly. "Helene Vetsera told us of his feigned death on the day of our departure from Trieste."

Countess Larisch and Agnes watched in silence as the girl gaped at the Empress.

"Papa!" she again suddenly shouted. "Where is he? When will Papa be here?"

Tears of joy intermingled with laughter as she stood up and embraced all three women.

"This is wonderful news!" she squealed. "I cannot wait to see him again!"

Countess Larisch smiled at Empress Elizabeth. Without saying a word to one another, both knew that they must never give up the search for John Vecera, father of Mary.

The messenger began his quest for John the following morning, and the four ladies from Austria waited and prayed for a fast and positive outcome.

Several days later, the four women were assigned to new quarters in the hotel. Hour after hour passed with Mary seated near the window, waiting and watching for her father's safe return. The news had produced an affirmative attitude in her. She was radiantly alive, gaining strength and color with each passing hour. Her boundless enthusiasm was contagious to the others who waited and watched with her. Buried memories of her father were scant and ambiguous from the passage of time. But they were beautiful. She said to them that she recalled her brother Ladislaus and sister Hanna telling her, "Papa travels. He goes to many exciting places!"

"Then," Mary explained, "when I was older they showed me a world globe and pointed to his location. That is when I began to understand his absence for months at a time."

Countess Larisch enjoyed hearing the sparse memories that were returning to the girl child of Baron Vetsera.

"Papa always brought me special gifts when he returned from his travels," Mary said softly. "Many times, he brought beautiful dolls and pretty dresses from faraway lands for Hanna and me."

Suddenly Mary stopped chattering and stared at the floor. The altered demeanor caused Countess Larisch to tense with concern. She glanced at Empress Elizabeth before reverting her attention back to Mary.

"Then," Mary said quietly, "when I was eight-years-old, the presents stopped coming, and I never saw Papa again. Mama got a telegram stating that he had died in Cairo from heart failure. Then, later, Mama received a message of condolence from Emperor Franz Josef, praising my father for seventeen years of unmarred and loyal service to the throne."

Again Mary paused, seemingly lost amid visions of days gone by.

"I remember Mama and us children moving to the Baltazzi Mansion after the news of Papa's death. It was there that I learned proper etiquette and gained my love for horses."

Her eyes sparkled with the recollection. "My uncle was well known for his fine horses," she grinned. "I respected and loved him very much. My uncles would take me with them to the race track and introduce me to the famous nobility. They told me that the aristocrats thought I was beautiful," she smiled. "But I think they liked to see me attired in the latest Paris fashions."

Mary seemed to be talking to herself as she continued dreaming, "I have sat beside the Prince of Wales and visited with numerous Countess's. They called me The Turf Angel," she added with a smile.

Again Mary fell silent. A look of melancholy suddenly darkened her mood, and she sighed.

"At age sixteen, I met my beloved Rudi for the first time. We were at Freudenau, a race track near Vienna."

No one spoke nor moved as the young girl trembled and rose to her feet. Her face was ashen. She walked to her room and gently closed the door behind her. The flame from the oil lamp cast eerie shadows among the sparse furnishings of the quarters.

The passage of time seemed cruel and foreboding in the Galveston, Texas hotel room. The Austrian exiled could now only helplessly await word from the phantom Baron who had left them so long ago.

FOURTEEN

Several days passed without word from the messenger or John Vecera. A cloud of fear and depression crept into the hearts of those who waited and kept watch on the dusty street below. Mary was now overcome with hopelessness and she often stared at the ceiling from her bed, her face void of all expression.

Thus, it came to pass, however, that Mary, Empress Elizabeth, Countess Larisch, and Agnes witnessed the arrival of a large covered-wagon. Late one afternoon, a team of attractive, gray horses were reined to a halt in front of the hotel. A husky man jumped from his rig and rushed inside the hotel, stopping only momentarily at the desk to inquire about a room number. He skipped many steps as he ran up the stairway to their door.

Countess Larisch was brushing her hair when a loud knock resounded through the chamber. Agnes quickly scurried across the room to answer it.

"Be careful, Agnes," the Countess whispered.

She laid the brush down on the dressing table and listened as Agnes inquired, "Who is it?"

"John Vecera," a deep voice responded. "I received word that my daughter is here."

Agnes quickly unbolted the lock and opened the door. Consternation etched his brow as he burst into the room and stared at the maid.

"Where is Mary?" he said gruffly. "The message said she would be here!"

Countess Larisch hurried toward him.

"I am Countess Marie Larisch, and I am so relieved that you are here!"

"Yes," he said after a brief pause.

His voice was calmer as he added, "Yes, I remember you, Countess."

Although addressing the Countess, his eyes darted about the room.

He smiled as he focused on the young girl who was quietly standing on the opposite side of the room.

"Mary?" he whispered. "Are you my Mary?"

"Yes, Papa," she replied breathlessly. "It is me. Mary."

"I cannot believe it," he exclaimed.

He walked slowly across the room toward her.

"My dear daughter, I did not think that I would ever see you again."

Countess Larisch felt relief well up within her as the father and child laughed and embraced. She glanced at Empress Elizabeth who was standing in silence beside the window.

I wonder what she is feeling at this moment, the Countess mused. *Fear? Relief? Dread? Or perhaps love?*

Mary grasped her father's neck as he picked her up in his arms and embraced her.

A moment later, he noticed the figure standing near the window.

"Empress Elizabeth!" he gasped. "This cannot be."

He slowly released his grip on Mary, and she slid down until her feet silently touched the floor. The moment seemed frozen in time as the exiled Baron Vetsera and Empress Elizabeth looked at one another.

"Come, Papa," Mary said softly. "Sit down."

"You must be exhausted from your long journey, John," Empress Elizabeth calmly said.

John's eyes did not leave the face of the Empress as he followed Mary to a chair and sat down.

"I do not understand . . ." he began.

"Agnes, John must be famished from his long journey," the Empress interrupted. "Please go to the dining room and bring sandwiches, pastries, and coffee for us."

As Agnes quickly departed, Empress Elizabeth and Countess Larisch moved to the settee and sat down.

"My good man, you don't know how important it is that we have found you," the Empress said. Then in a calm, even voice she continued. "John, I have much to tell you. I will begin by saying that the four of us have been exiled to America."

John stared at the Empress in disbelief before glancing at Countess Larisch and Mary.

"It is true, Baron Vetsera," the Countess said. "We are banished from Austria, and, like you, we must never return."

Mary sat down on the arm of John's chair with her hand resting on his shoulder. He listened without intervention as Empress Elizabeth related some of the details of the past eight years. Twenty minutes had passed before a faint knock interrupted the conversation. Countess Larisch quickly responded to the summons.

"I am here with the food and drink," Agnes said softly. The Countess opened the door, allowing the maid to enter with the heavily laden tray.

While they ate, John inquired about family members and friends. The conversation was lighthearted as everyone reminisced over fun and happy times that they had shared in the past. When the five finished the meal, Agnes quickly gathered the dishes and stacked them on the tray.

"You are looking very tired, Baroness Mary," the maid commented.

"Yes," Countess Larisch agreed. "You really should get some rest."

Mary glanced at her father before appealing to the Empress and the Countess.

"But, I am not tired," she said.

"You get some rest now, Mary," John said with a smile. "I will not leave. I promise."

As Mary and Agnes left the room together, John leaned back in his chair.

"Continue, Empress. I know that there is much more that you have not yet told me."

Countess Larisch nodded, and the Empress again resumed speaking.

"Yes, John. There is much more."

As twilight faded into the blackness of night, the matriarch told of the bitter dissension between Emperor Franz Josef and Crown Prince Rudolph, describing Rudolph's profound desire to reign over Hungary. Her eyes glistened with pride as she spoke of his love for the country and the Hungarian people, paying special tribute to his loving and loyal following.

"About this time, a beautiful young lady came into Rudolph's life," Empress Elizabeth quietly continued. "It soon became apparent that their relationship was more than casual, and the Emperor would not tolerate a full-fledged love affair. At this point, he beckoned me to discuss the matter."

Empress Elizabeth paused before quietly adding, "Yes, John. The young lady, whom I speak of, is our daughter Mary."

John covered his eyes and groaned when she finally told of the clandestine affair between Rudolph and Mary.

"In desperation, I told Baroness Helene of their affair and suggested that she take Mary on an extended vacation. They went to London to see Hanna. And, when the rumors subsided, they returned. The separation was to no avail."

Empress Elizabeth paused and lowered her gaze. Countess Larisch patted her gently on her clasped hands.

"Go on," the Countess quietly encouraged. "John must know. Everything."

The matron nodded and began to speak again.

"Baroness Helene then took Mary to Paris. While there, Mary corresponded with her French teacher, Monsieur Dubray, in Payerbach. Through him, Rudolph and Mary conveyed messages, continually validating their love for one another. Rudolph requested that the Pope grant him annulment from his marriage to Stephanie, the Emperor's choice for his mate. Although unable to bear a male heir to the throne, Stephanie informed the Emperor that she would not relinquish her title to Mary Vetsera, a commoner."

John leaned forward in his chair and started to speak. But, deciding against it, he shook his head and leaned back.

Countess Larisch drew a deep breath and looked at Empress Elizabeth. Her facial expression was grim, but John's reaction did not hinder her from proceeding.

"Your wife and daughters were invited to attend a birthday dinner party for Wilhelm II at Schunnbrun Castle. Although Rudolph was at Mayerling at that time, he insisted that the Vetsera family receive an invitation. Stephanie was there when Mary arrived.

Empress Elizabeth basked within the memory for a brief moment.

"Our daughter was beautiful that evening," she sighed. "She was attired in a pale blue dress and yellow floral appliques. Indeed, she captivated everyone's attention with her youthful beauty."

John smiled appreciatively at the proud mother.

"Yes," he agreed with a nod. "I am quite sure that she did."

"Later in the evening, the festivities were momentarily disrupted when Princess Stephanie and Mary met face to face. Our young Baroness refused to curtsy or acknowledge the Austrian Crown Princess as nobility. Thus, the following day,

Princess Stephanie complained to Emperor Franz Josef. Shortly thereafter, he learned of . . ."

Tears suddenly spilled down the cheeks of the Empress. Countess Larisch quickly reached for a linen handkerchief from the dresser and handed it to the matron.

"Forgive me, John," she said, "but this is so hard to share with you."

John leaned forward and patted her hand.

"I understand," he said softly. "But I am unable to help if I do not know the truth."

Empress Elizabeth dabbed the tears from her face and cleared a lump from her throat. "No one took the affair seriously," she proceeded, "until it became too late. Meanwhile, the Emperor's spies learned of the treacherous act being plotted against him and they knew it had to be stopped. Count Edward Von Taaffe, the prime minister was ordered to take action.

"Shortly thereafter, Emperor Franz Josef was told of the babe that had been conceived by Rudolph and Mary. And, within a short while, he issued the mandate. Crown Prince Rudolph was to be assassinated under the guise of a double suicide."

"Babe?" John said in a loud voice. "Baby?" he repeated, "But where is the child?"

Empress Elizabeth raised her hand to silence him.

"The child is not yet born, John. Mary may very well be carrying the next rightful heir to the throne of Austria."

Countess Larisch stood up and walked to the window. The air in the room suddenly felt hot and humid, comparable to the tragedy that was being related by the Empress of Austria. She gazed down at the now slumbering frontier seaport of Galveston. A tear escaped down her cheek as she listened to the quiet discussion that was taking place behind her.

"Dedicated to his Emperor, Prime Minister Edward Von Taaffe felt honored to be the dominating figure in the assassination of Rudolph and Mary and their unborn child. He disliked Rudi intensely. Baron Krauss said that Rudolph arrived at his hunting lodge in Mayerling on the weekend of the twenty-seventh as planned. His driver, Bradfisch, had been instructed to deliver Mary to Mayerling, under the pretense of Rudolph's personal request, two days after the arrival of the Crown Prince."

Empress Elizabeth paused to catch her breath.

"Please, Empress," John entreated, "please continue."

"But," she said in a smooth and straightforward tone, "their original hastily concocted plan backfired when Mary did not die as planned. And that, John, is the reason that the four of us are in America hiding like criminals."

The door suddenly opened and Mary walked back into the room.

"I simply cannot rest at this moment," she said. "Not when I haven't seen my Papa for so long."

John smiled broadly. "Of course. I think everyone will be able to forgive you this time."

No one objected, for no one could deny the strong yearning produced by such an important reunion.

"Tell me, Mary" John asked, "Why did you agree to the journey to Mayerling?"

"My Dear Papa," she said as she again took her position on the arm of John's chair, "when the Countess put me in the carriage with Bradfisch as my driver and escort, I felt secure and rather excited about seeing Rudi again. When we arrived at the lodge, Bradfisch helped me out of the carriage and swung the large entrance gate open. I saw Rudi waiting for me near his quarters, and I ran through the snow to meet him."

John patted his daughter's hand and asked quickly, "And then?"

"Rudi was surprised that I was there. 'What are you doing here, Mary?' he asked. 'Did you not summon me?' I responded."

"He put his arm over my shoulder, and the two of us turned toward the coach. It was hidden behind the tea house. Bradfisch was aiming a pistol at us. Rudi tried to pull me inside, but I heard shots. I saw his head shattered."

Mary paused and swallowed to repel a rising hysteria.

"His blood and portions of his brain flew all over me. And then, I felt something hot hit my head, and I fell on the snow next to Rudi. I recall that the blood turned the snow crimson and it felt warm. I spotted Rudi's hand near mine. I tried to grasp it, but I was only able to touch his fingertips before losing consciousness."

John smoothed the hair back from her eyes and gently touched her cheek.

"The next thing that I remember is awakening. Several people were standing over me, and I heard many voices. One said, 'She must not be found here. Dead or alive!' Then they carried me into the woodshed beside the servant's wing of the lodge. They put me in a large clothes basket and covered me with piles of blankets. The voices said that I could remain there until the doctor arrived. When I regained consciousness for the second time, I was wet and cold. A doctor and my Uncle Alexander and Uncle Georg were trying to wash off the blood. I was not in pain at that time, but the numbness frightened me. Even though my senses were quiet dulled I couldn't help being humiliated and ashamed. I heard someone say, 'Hurry, get her ready quickly. She must be taken away immediately.'

"I was then carried off and placed in a carriage. My uncles sat on each side of me. I felt weak and let my head rest on Uncle Alexander's shoulder. The carriage hurriedly sped away. There was darkness and I could not see, nor hear anyone mention where we were going. Sometime later the carriage stopped. I heard voices, many voices, and arguments. Soon my uncle's had taken me into a dark room. It felt good when I was placed on a bed and warmly covered up. Before I fell asleep, I could hear rain beating heavily on the roof and the winds howling excessively.

"It seemed only a short time later at just before day break, that I again was brought into the carriage and once more whisked away. Before we departed, a monk prayed over me and wished me well. I realized then that I had been spending time in a monastery. By the time we left, I was in excruciating pain. There was a terrible hurt and buzzing in my head. I was dizzy and nauseous, and then it seemed as if I slept for days.

As Mary turned away from him, John stood up.

"What a horrifying experience you all have had," he said huskily. "Tomorrow I will take you home. You all must rest now, for the journey will take us all day."

Countess Larisch did not turn around when John quietly withdrew from the quarters. As though mesmerized by the tale of treachery, the lady stared at fireflies who were dancing among the subtropical foliage below. A sad smile appeared on her lips as her gaze slowly moved upward toward the starlit heavens.

"Home," she muttered to herself. "I wonder if we shall ever know the true meaning of the word again. May God show us the way."

A cricket sang a melancholy ode to the night, blending with the whispered plea, "And may we not stumble or fall during our exodus to freedom in a new land."

PART II

VOWS OF SILENCE

TEXAS
AMERICA

FIFTEEN

A THUNDERHEAD BILLOWED ABOVE THE HORIZON OF THE GULF of Mexico, laced with a silver lining from the rising sun. A ship's whistle sounded in the distance as the four ladies and one man sat down in the dining room to eat a hot breakfast before departing from Galveston. The mood and conversation was lighthearted throughout the meal, and they left the table with renewed faith and optimism.

Soon, trunks and belongings were loaded into John's covered-wagon for the long journey to LaGrange. Mary sat on the wagon seat with John on the right and Empress Elizabeth on the left. A barrage of questions poured forth from her as the large pair of gray horses trotted through the bustling seaport. Countess Larisch and Agnes stood up and peered over the heads of Mary and her parents. All five people in the wagon were now modestly attired in the clothes of commoners. The morning air felt cool and refreshing to Countess Larisch as the big wagon left Galveston and took a northwest route inland.

"It is wonderful to hear the birds again," the Countess remarked. "Even that black one that sounds like a rusty gate."

Everyone laughed and looked at the bedraggled bird that was standing beside the road.

"It is called a grackle," John explained with a chuckle. "You will be pleased to hear that America offers prettier and more melodious fowl than this."

Throughout the afternoon hours, John shared the names of various birds, trees, and foliage, and the Austrian ladies happily absorbed the knowledge. And thus, the hours passed quickly as the covered-wagon rolled across the miles toward their new home.

The sun was setting on the horizon when John suddenly checked the reins, and the wagon creaked to a halt.

"There it is, Ladies," he said proudly. "There is your new home!"

No one spoke for a moment. The house looked tiny and stark between the vast expanse of farmland. Although near the town of LaGrange, the farmstead appeared lonely and forlorn within a sea of cultivation.

"Oh, Papa," Mary said with astonishment. "It is so. . . it is so . . . so small!"

"Small, Mary?" John asked. "You feel that it is *too* small?"

"Yes, Papa. It is very small for the five of us."

John looked at each one of the women before picking up the reins of the team.

"It will look larger. When we arrive at the front porch you will see that it is indeed adequate housing for the five of us."

Soon, trunks and belongings were carried into the abode. Countess Larisch tried to help Agnes organize and sort out the possessions. As the maid pulled a dress from the baggage, the pungent scent of mildew permeated the room.

"Whew, it smells musty," the Countess groaned. "It may take some work and time to remove the voyage from our lives."

"Yes, it will, Agnes agreed with a grin. "But, I am so thankful to be off the ship and on land again. The cleanup will be a pleasure."

Countess Larisch looked around the cramped quarters and shook her head.

"As Mary said 'this is so . . .so. . .small!'"

The two ladies looked at one another and burst into laughter.

"What is so funny?"

John's deep voice quieted the outburst to muffled giggles.

"We were just sharing our delight over being on land rather than water," the Countess laughed. "It seems that our wardrobes have inherited the unpleasant odor of a fish!"

The unexpected comment caused John to laugh. Suddenly he grew serious and looked around the room.

"Mary was right," he finally agreed. "This house is indeed too small."

The Countess and Agnes looked at one another. Then they burst into laughter again, but this time they were joined at once by the man of the house.

"I will start looking for larger living quarters in the morning," he sputtered.

True to his word, at daybreak the following morning, the Austrian gentleman departed from the farmstead in search of tangible living quarters for him and the ladies. But, at dusk that evening, he walked into the house and shook his head.

"I found nothing suitable today," he said. "But tomorrow, I will try again."

Several days passed with John leaving each morning and returning each evening to no avail. One afternoon, Mary was sweeping off the front porch when she saw her father approaching.

"Come quickly!" she called to the other women. "Papa is coming. He is in a gallop. Perhaps he has good news for us."

Countess Larisch, Empress Elizabeth, and Agnes joined Mary on the porch as the Austrian gentleman reined his horse to a halt.

"You will not believe what I found today, my ladies," he said with a wide grin.

He dismounted and tied his tall, lean saddled horse to the hitching post.

"Did you find a larger home for us, Papa?" Mary inquired.

"Indeed I did, my child," he laughed. "I found a spacious and beautiful home for us near Muldoon. The architecture will remind you of our homes in Vienna!"

"John," gasped Empress Elizabeth. "It sounds lovely, but why would anyone want to sell a house such as this?"

"The owner completed the construction of it, but then he experienced insurmountable financial difficulties and has to sell. The estate is perfect for us!"

Within twenty-four hours, meager household goods and belongings were packed in the covered-wagon, and the little band of Austrian's left the homestead near LaGrange for their new home near Muldoon.

Squeals of delight filled the air as the wagon rolled past the huge oak and pine trees and stopped in front of the house. The white, two story structure had an abundance of windows. Both upper and lower floors were encircled with large verandas, overlooking trees and beautiful native foliage.

"Oh, Papa," Mary gasped. "It looks just like our home at Payerbach!"

John smiled and embraced his daughter.

"I thought you would approve."

Happy exclamations of agreement came forth from each woman as the little group entered the house. Empress Elizabeth quickly decided on the east bedroom for her quarters.

"It is beautiful," she said. "And I will once again be able to enjoy the rising sun from the veranda outside of my bedroom."

"Perfect," Countess Larisch agreed enthusiastically. "And in the evening you can move to the west veranda to enjoy the twilight."

Empress Elizabeth smiled and said, "Yes. That will be perfect. The west veranda in the evening, enjoying my pipe and perhaps a glass of whiskey. We are indeed home."

Agnes went straight to the kitchen, while Mary and Countess Larisch wandered through the beautiful house, planning their decorative strategy.

"The oval portrait of Empress Elizabeth must be put over the fireplace," Mary said.

"Yes," the Countess agreed. "That is the ideal place for it."

"But what should we do about draperies and furniture, Countess?" Mary asked. "We do not have anything to put in this magnificent home."

Suddenly a deep chuckle from across the room interrupted their conversation. John was standing in the doorway with his arms folded, watching and listening to their excited chatter.

"You will be able to order any fabric in any color that you choose for the drapes," he said with a smile.

He ambled toward them adding, "The shopkeeper also has a wide variety of fabric for clothing. I will take you there whenever you so desire. And furniture is available too."

"It seems as if we are in a world of our own, Papa," Mary said quietly. "I love it, but how far is it to town?"

"There is a church and a store several miles away in the town of Plum. You are quite right, Mary. We are secluded."

"Emperor Franz Josef would be pleased to know that we are living our lives in obscurity," Countess Larisch declared.

"Yes, perhaps he would," John agreed. "Although I doubt that he would approve of the home and life-style that we are acquiring. He may have preferred that we suffer in our banishment."

Relaxed and fun-filled days passed with the five reassembling their lives. John selected a horse for Empress Elizabeth to ride, and she basked in the outings on horseback. The Countess watched and smiled as the lady reclaimed her love for poetry, both perusing and writing the beloved verse.

One day, John escorted Empress Elizabeth and Countess Larisch to the nearest large town for the finest furniture available. John and the Empress laughed and talked throughout the journey. True serenity was evident in the eyes of the Empress. She had indeed found peace and happiness at last.

Our Empress is truly vibrant with life, the Countess mused. *It seems as though she is the Phoenix, rising from the ashes of Austria to live and thrive once again in the freedom of America. It is wonderful!*

During dinner one evening, the conversation turned to their shared vow of silence and the transformation their lives had taken.

"Empress Elizabeth, you seem so much happier now," Countess Larisch said with a smile.

Suddenly John slapped the table with his hand.

"That is what we have failed to do!"

The unexpected outburst startled the four women, and they all turned to stare at the gentleman who was now standing.

"John," Countess Larisch said. "Are you all right?"

"Calm down, John," Empress Elizabeth said quietly. "What is it that we have failed to do?"

"You must all change your names," he said in a calmer voice. "We cannot live in obscurity with an Empress Elizabeth, a Countess Larisch, and a Baroness Vetsera among us."

John sat back down as murmurs of agreement echoed through the dining room.

Empress Elizabeth stood up and looked at each person seated at the table.

"My name is Frances," she said firmly and sat down.

A moment later, Agnes stood up.

"My name is Annie," she declared and sat down.

Countess Larisch stood up.

"I will retain my given name Marie," she stated. "It seems to be a common name in this country and should not raise undue suspicion. But I am no longer the Countess."

For a moment the room was silent. Everyone looked at Mary, but the girl did not move.

"And, my daughter," John said quietly as the Countess sat down. "What about you?"

"Papa, Mary is also a common name in America," she said as she rose to her feet. Her eyes glistened as she looked at each one. "I am Mary Vecera, daughter of John Vecera."

"Very well," John said as he stood to his feet. "I would like to propose a toast."

He lifted his glass to each lady.

"Frances Vecera," he said. "Annie Vecera, Marie Vecera, and Mary Vecera. Welcome to America, Ladies."

And thus, the lives and identities of those expelled from Austria began anew. That evening, titles were forsaken with John and Frances Vecera symbolizing man and wife. The scenario was complete, and the vow of silence duly executed.

SIXTEEN

THE HOME AND LIFE-STYLE OF THE AUSTRIAN VECERA ASSEMblage were once again aristocratic and noble. Each member quickly adjusted and settled in their American frontier home near Muldoon, Texas. Marie Larisch felt comfortable with their pristine identities, basking in the blissful calm that prevailed within the Empress, Frances Vecera.

"And that Annie is so happy here!" Marie chuckled one day as she descended the stairs, "She is truly having fun in that big kitchen, creating strange but delicious culinary fares with a hint of Vienna in each one."

"Good morning, Annie," she called, as she entered the kitchen.

However, the servant did not respond. She checked the walk-in pantry and peeked out of the kitchen door, but the maid was not in her usual domain. Marie shrugged and poured herself a cup of coffee.

I must have awakened early this morning, she mistakenly thought as she passed through the empty sitting room and walked outside onto the veranda. Marie sat down and put her cup on the white wicker table next to her seat. She sighed and leaned back, watching a blue jay flit among the greenery of an elm tree.

When the kitchen screen door opened and closed, she glanced to her right. Annie suddenly appeared at the corner of the house. Her face mirrored fatigue and dejection. She sat down near the Countess.

"Marie," she said quietly, "Did you hear Mary during the night?"

"Yes, I did," Marie replied. "But my room is so far away from her that I seldom hear when she has a bad dream. Are the nightmares more frequent and severe now, Annie?"

Annie nodded and sighed before leaning back in her chair. A mockingbird landed on a branch nearby, singing a soft, melodious song to the morning. As though on cue, a squirrel darted across the grass with an acorn clenched in his teeth and ran up a tree.

"Life in America is good," Marie said quietly, "but I fear that Mary may suffer from the memory of the assassination and the bullet wound for some time to come."

Annie flinched and moved to the edge of her chair.

"Has she mentioned her terrible headaches to you?" Annie asked.

"No. But I have seen her lying down on her bed in the middle of the day with a damp cloth over her eyes."

Marie took a sip of coffee before softly adding, "Perhaps time will heal her both mentally and physically."

The maid nodded and rose to her feet.

"I will pray for her deliverance from pain," she said quietly. "I must go in now. There is much to do and it will soon be time to begin preparations for lunch."

Seconds later, Marie heard the door close as Annie re-entered the kitchen. She rested her head on the back of the chair and closed her eyes.

"Good morning, Marie."

John's voice filtered through her troubled thoughts, and she sat up and looked around.

She watched him as he walked up the steps of the veranda. His stride did not have its normal vigor, and his eyes were clouded with fatigue and worry. His normal proud poise was lost as he slumped down on the chair next to Marie.

"Rough night?" Marie softly queried.

John sat up and leaned toward the Countess.

"I don't know what to do about Mary," he said hoarsely. "Her nightmares wake me up every night. I hear her screaming 'Rudolph!' or 'Rudi!' but when I run to her room, she will not talk to me. She just lays there, sobbing and shaking. Last night I could not get her calmed down, Marie. I am exhausted, and I am very concerned about her mental state."

"My room is too far away for me to hear her," Marie repeated. "I usually wake up when everyone else is already up and running. Would you like to trade bedrooms for a while, John? At least you may get a decent night of sleep."

"No thank you, Marie," he said quietly. "But I do appreciate the offer."

He stood up and stretched.

"It sounds reasonably quiet at the moment," he quipped. "I believe that I can stand a short nap before lunch. I have been up for hours."

Marie finished her coffee and followed him into the house. Frances was coming down the stairs as they entered. She was yawning, and dark circles were evident beneath her eyes.

Something must be done about Mary, Marie mused, *and soon! I will try to stay awake tonight and help with her.*

But, the following days did not improve. Their lives became an unbearable illusion of somber reality. Nerves became frayed, patience wore thin, and everyone began to dread the dark hours. Screams of pain and torment echoed against the stillness of each night, while those awakened, blindly attempted to help.

One morning, Marie and Annie met on the veranda with their coffee. Both women were silent for a time. Their faces were lined with worry and exhaustion.

"We have to do something," Annie whispered. "None of us can handle this much longer."

Marie touched Annie on the shoulder and said, "I will question her about the headaches and the bad dreams, Annie. Perhaps there is something we can do to stop them."

The maid nodded and stood up.

"Thank you, Countess . . . I mean, Marie. Let me know if I can do anything more. I have some ladanum left in the pantry, but I have been afraid to offer it."

Marie smiled. "I will let you know, Annie. Thank you."

Frances was reading a book of poetry when Marie entered the house.

"How are you today, Frances? Did you get any sleep last night?"

The matron looked up at Marie and slowly shook her head. "I am concerned for us and Mary," she said. "I heard her screaming again during the night, and she was sitting up in her bed. She seemed so frightened and in such pain! Once again, I dampened a cloth and wiped the perspiration from her brow, but she would not talk to me." Tears trickled down her face, and she turned away.

"Annie and I were just discussing the severity of our dilemma," Marie said in a calm, reassuring voice. "I will try talking to her again."

"Please do," Frances agreed. "My nights have become so short and disrupted that I cannot sleep unless Mary is resting quietly."

"I will try talking to her right now, Frances," Marie replied with a smile. "Try to get some rest, and I will insist that she talk about her difficulties. And then perhaps we will all sleep better tonight."

Marie stood up and squared her shoulders. With a determined expression on her face, she left the study and walked up the stairs, pausing only briefly beside Mary's door.

"Who is it?" Mary responded in an annoyed tone.

"Marie," she replied. "May I come in for a moment?"

"I guess. But please do not stay long. I have a terrible headache."

Marie entered the darkened room and waited for her eyesight to adjust before walking over to the bed.

"How long since the headaches have returned, Mary?" she asked quietly.

Mary turned away with her face to the wall and said in a muffled voice, "I think that I have had them all of my life."

Marie sat down on the edge of the bed.

"And the nightmares, Mary?" she queried. "How long have you been having nightmares?"

Mary glared at Marie.

"Since Rudi . . . Oh never mind. I don't want to talk about it!"

The girl again turned to face the wall. Marie waited for a moment before rising to her feet. She shook her head and left the room.

Frances and Annie were waiting for her as she descended the stairs.

"What did you find out?" Frances inquired. "Were you able to talk to her?"

Frances and Annie followed as Marie slowly walked across the room. She shrugged and shook her head before walking out of the door and onto the veranda. Again, the two women followed her.

"John was so upset this morning that he went into town to get away from the nightmarish hysteria of Mary," Frances said. "He is going to confer with a physician, regarding her suffering. I wonder, though, what good even *that* will do."

Marie stared at her hands without speaking for one full minute. Frances and Annie glanced at one another several times, hoping and waiting for guidance from the Countess.

Suddenly Marie stood up and, without uttering one word, walked back into the house. She again ascended the stairs and went to Mary's door. This time, the Countess did not knock and wait for acceptance into the room. She left the door open and walked straight to the other side of the chamber. Sunlight streamed in as she pulled back the drapes and opened the window. A cool breeze rustled the edge of the window covering as though breathing lifeblood back into the room.

Marie sat down on the edge of the bed and said, "We are going to talk about your nightmares, Mary. And then, we are going to discuss the frequent headaches that you have been experiencing. And," she added sternly, "then we are going to find a solution for both."

Mary slowly pulled a damp cloth from her forehead. She blinked against the unaccustomed light and sat up. Marie sat quietly and watched as the girl slowly swung her legs over the side of the bed and stood up.

"Thank you, Countess Marie," she said. "I need help."

Tears streamed down Mary's face as Marie embraced her. The two sobbed and rocked back and forth, sharing relentless pain. Throughout the following hour, Mary shared the nightly recurrence of Rudolph's death. She spoke of the emptiness in her heart, and the pain she felt from his lost love.

"And, when the horrid vision of him on the snow in a pool of blood fades for a moment," she gasped, "my head fills with agonizing pain."

Marie released her grip on the young Baroness. She put her hands on each side of her face and said, "Mary, you will recover. I will help you. The Empress, Annie, and your father will help you, and you will heal. Grief from the loss of a loved one subsides with time, my dear Mary. You must remember that Rudolph will always be a part of you. He loved you with all of his heart, and nothing can take that away from you. Do you understand, Mary? Rudolph has left a part of himself with you."

"Yes," Mary said appreciatively. "Nothing can change our love for one another."

"That's right," Marie said firmly. "And when visions of sad times enter your mind, fight it. Replace the bad with memories of the wonderful times that you shared. Rudolph would be pleased with your choice."

A faint smile appeared on Mary's face as she again embraced Marie.

"Thank you," she said. "I truly believe that I can replace the nightmares with the sweet recollection of our love."

Marie picked up the brush from the dressing table and gently smoothed the hair away from Mary's face.

"Now, let's go downstairs and discuss your headaches with the others. We will find the cure for them, Mary. And we will do it as a family."

The Countess and the young Baroness walked down the stairs together and went through the house to the veranda. Frances and Annie joyously greeted Mary as she stepped into the sunlight and smiled.

Standing there gazing at the sky, Mary could only reminisce over the happy moments with Rudolph. Those times of togetherness, stolen as they were, were certainly not forgotten nor regretted. The pledges of love they had made to each other she could never break.

SEVENTEEN

Everyone rode to town with Mary for her first appointment with an American physician. Annie went to the general store for supplies, and John went to the barber shop for a hair cut and shave while Mary, Frances, and Marie met with the doctor.

Mary immediately began to complain. "I am having great difficulty with my hearing, and my head hurts most of the time! What is this constant buzzing in my ears?"

"We shall see, Mary," the doctor said, "We shall see."

After giving the new patient a thorough checkup, he motioned for the three ladies to be seated. They anxiously waited for the doctor's prognosis.

"Mary's headaches and the ringing in her ears seem to be due to the quinine she was given aboard ship for her infection and high temperature."

Countess Marie felt her pulse quicken, and she looked at the Empress through a veil of guilt.

"We saved both of their lives, did we not?" Frances said in a hushed but firm manner.

All Mary could offer was a vacant stare.

The doctor put his hand on her shoulder and said reassuringly, "Well, no matter now. I'm sure your symptoms will be gone soon. I want you to drink this now, Mary. It is a sedative that will help settle your nerves."

He handed her a glass of liquid, and she quickly drank it.

"Thank you, Doctor," the ladies murmured in unison as they turned and left his office.

But with the passage of days and weeks, Mary's headaches became more severe, and her hearing was rapidly deteriorating. Again, she was taken to the doctor.

"The buzzing in her head will eventually disappear," he maintained after the Countess admitted administering the extra dose of quinine. "But, she will also experience a great deal of hearing loss."

The doctor hesitated before turning to his patient and adding, "This damage to your hearing is permanent. You will never regain what is lost."

Marie hurried to Mary's side as tears began to flow, unchecked, down her face. She kept an arm around her as the doctor continued.

"You must be grateful that you still have your baby, Mary," he said consolingly. "It is a true miracle that you did not miscarry during the voyage. The amount of quinine that you ingested would normally induce termination of the baby."

John had sat quietly throughout the prognosis, but now he stood up and addressed the physician.

"What can we do to help her?"

"Well, there is one thing," the doctor replied. "There is a school in Austin for the deaf. The facility teaches their hearing impaired students sign language and lip reading. This art of communication is invaluable."

"I don't want to go!" Mary cried. "I want to stay at home with my family."

"Do not fret about it now, Mary," Frances said. "There will be plenty of time to think about it."

As the ladies left the doctor's office, John remained to inquire further about the school in Austin. Moments later, he joined them at the wagon without commenting further on the subject.

Two weeks later, John received word from the Deaf School in Austin. Mary had indeed been accepted into their boarding facility. He excitedly shared the news with his daughter, hoping she would have a change of heart.

"But I do not want to go!" Mary insisted. "Life would be frightening away from you and living at a school like that. I do not want to go, Papa."

John dropped the subject until Mary had retired for the night. Then, he, Marie, and Frances quietly discussed the matter in the sitting room.

"Indeed, the tutoring would be invaluable to her, John," the Empress agreed. "She should go. Besides, it might just be an excellent place to hide from certain malevolent-minded parties. We must not forget that Mary is carrying a child who could pose a threat to the throne of Austria."

John abandoned his chair and paced across the room as Frances continued.

"It is improbable that the Emperor will send spies to a school for the deaf. But I would put nothing past him in his search for Mary and her baby. All of us must hope that she will remain secure and safe during her training at the school."

John and Marie murmured in agreement.

"I feel that you alone should escort our daughter to the school, John," the matron continued, "just to be on the safe side. If we are already under surveillance by the monarch, Marie, Annie, and I would do better to remain here. Mary's new sanctuary could more easily be exposed by all of us going."

John glanced at the Empress and the Countess before assenting.

"Yes, I alone will take Mary to Austin. Tell Annie to draft a list of supplies for me to bring back so that I do not return with an empty wagon."

"If you wish, I will speak with Mary in depth about the positive benefits of the school," Marie offered quietly. "It will help all of us if she leaves in good spirits."

"Thank you, Countess," Frances said.

She closed her eyes and rested her head on the back of the chair. John put his hand on the shoulder of the sorrowful Empress and nodded.

"Yes, Marie," he softly agreed. "Thank you."

And thus, the plan for the deliverance of their young Baroness to the school for the deaf in Austin was conceived.

As she had promised, Marie discussed the matter more thoroughly with Mary. There were some trying moments, but in the end Mary reluctantly nodded her approval.

The day for departure soon arrived. Preparation for the journey was limited by the rules and regulations of the institute. The personal possessions of students were restricted to long, white dresses and bare essentials, so the chore of packing was minimal for Annie. But it was also heartfelt. Marie sat on the bed beside Mary as the belongings were folded and stored in a modest bag. When the final item was put in place, Mary again burst into tears.

"I cannot live like this!" she wailed.

"This stark way of living is only temporary," Marie reminded her. "You will return before you know it."

Mary hesitantly agreed as she followed Annie and Marie out of the bedroom and descended the stairs. When they arrived on the veranda, Marie noted that John was standing beside Frances, patiently waiting to load the sparse baggage into the wagon. The Countess hesitated on the steps.

"Mary," Marie said. "Do you remember our conversation about this?"

Tears streamed down Mary's face as she nodded. Marie put her hands on each side of her friend's bewildered face, forcing her to gaze into her eyes.

"A new adventure, Mary. You will be coming home again, and this school is just a new and exciting adventure for you."

"Yes," Mary admitted. "An adventure. You are right, Countess. I will be fine."

Marie embraced Mary and watched her climb upon the seat beside her father. Then she quickly turned and walked toward Frances and Annie who were standing at the foot of the steps. As the wagon disappeared among the tall trees and foliage, she saw Mary look back and wave good-by.

The Vecera home was now veiled in a ghostly silence. Hearts were heavy over Mary facing the unknown without their personal love and guidance. Stability was maintained only through prayers and faith.

One evening at twilight, Marie joined Frances on the west veranda where the Empress was seated in her rocking chair, quietly puffing on her pipe.

"Good evening, Frances. Would you mind if I joined you for a moment?"

"Not at all," Frances smiled. "As a matter of fact, I am rather glad that you are here. My mind is traveling back in time. I was envisioning the first time that I relinquished my Mary. And the memory is not a happy one," she noted before taking a sip of whiskey.

"Yes," Marie said quickly. "And now she is gone again. It must be very painful. But," she added in a cheerful tone, "this time, she knows that you are her mother, and you love her very much."

"Yes, that is true."

The Empress puffed on her pipe and gazed at the pastel hues now fading from the heavens.

"I already yearn to receive a letter from her," she continued, "for I do miss her so."

"I believe we will all feel better when that day arrives," Marie agreed.

The two women suddenly fell silent; each one seizing the opportunity to reinstate subliminal hope. As darkness settled upon the Texas countryside, an owl welcomed the night with a soft, deep hoot. Tree frogs joined the ballad with a rhythmic chant of serenity.

Finally the Empress spoke as though talking to herself.

"One night my sister and I slipped out of our bedroom in our gowns. We walked a short distance away from the house and sat down on a rock. We watched the beautiful moon shining in all of its glory for a long time. We saw the sky, full of twinkling stars, and we wished for all of our dreams to come true."

As the Empress again became silent, Marie leaned back in her chair and closed her eyes. No response was needed nor wanted. The memory did not need to be tarnished with words.

The following days passed with Frances and Marie sharing a great deal of their time. They took long walks with the Empress relating to the days of her youth in Bavaria, roaming the fields barefoot and carefree. She spoke often of the large dog who was her constant companion.

Marie noted that Frances was drawn to the beauty of nature, finding solace in the same as she awaited news from Mary. The two women spent many hours in the flower garden, sharing moments from the past. Often, while walking through the woods, Marie waited as Frances sat down on a log with a pen and tablet. Within the beauty of nature, the Empress rapidly wrote down memoirs from her life. On one such occasion she penned:

> Oh, how I loved those tall trees. The evergreens and the flowers surrounding them were always so impressive. In the woods, the different greens were luxuriant. Thick clumps of wild flowers, strong and robust, burst out among the rocks as though the

> rocks were sending them forth. Around the mountains, the small meadows along the river were bathed with the most tender shades of green. The umbra of the mountains partially shaded the flowers that were so eagerly wanting to show their true colors. Spring at the Schunnbrun garden displayed a gorgeous array of vivid tones.

On several occasions, the matron remained seated for such long intervals that she was unable to stand alone. At such times, Marie would graciously assist her with one arm around the matron and thc other bearing the precious journal. While bedfast with rheumatism, Marie sat beside the Empress, listening to her share fleeting moments of happiness in Vienna. And time and again, Marie was reminded of the sincere love for nature that was indeed prevalent and foremost within the heart of the Empress.

EIGHTEEN

THE AUSTIN SCHOOL FOR THE DEAF LOOKED COLD AND FOREboding to Mary as her father reined the team to a halt. She leaned across the seat and kissed him on the cheek.

"I love you, Papa," she said softly.

She quickly leaned over and retrieved her little bundle of belongings and stepped down from the wagon.

It looks more like a prison than a school, she thought as she slowly started up the steps to the huge double doors. Suddenly the entire plan was overwhelming, and she paused halfway to the top.

"I cannot do this," she cried. "I feel that I have lost my family, and I have been sentenced to jail!"

She reached for the handrail. But, before her fingers touched the bar, she suddenly felt the warm, security of her father as he slipped his hand within her grasp.

"You are fine, Mary," he said soothingly. "I will walk beside you. Don't be afraid, my child. I am going with you."

Mary sat outside the office of the Mother Superior while John introduced himself and explained his daughter's circumstances and state of health.

"Just remember, Sister," he stressed, "Mary is not here only for her hearing problem, but as much so for her concealment—at least until after the birth of her child."

Soon a Sister was summoned, and she approached Mary with a warm smile.

"I have come to escort you to your quarters," she said.

Mary struggled to hear through the din of loud ringing in her ears. As the Nun motioned for her to follow, she rose to her feet and obediently fell into step behind the kind and helpful servant of God. Although appreciative of the cordial Nun during their walk, Mary felt small and vulnerable. The walls were drab and cold to the touch. The lack of elegance did not improve as she entered her small room. The quarters were stark and tiny, equipped only with a narrow closet, a small writing desk, and a bed.

After Mary declined an offer of help with unpacking, her escort graciously bowed and departed. Mary sat down on the cot and tightly held the little bundle of belongings against her chest.

Several minutes later, she heard a knock above the buzzing sound in her head. Before she could respond, the door opened, and the uninvited visitor entered the room.

"I am Sister Gabriel," a rather tall and attractive Nun said.

The Sister continued to speak, but Mary lost the words amid the ringing in her ears.

"Would you repeat that, please?" Mary said loudly. "I cannot understand what you are saying."

The Sister smiled and nodded. This time, as she spoke, her voice was loud and the words were spoken in a slow and precise manner.

"I am Sister Gabriel. I will be close at hand to assist you, Mary. My room is next to yours, so if you should ever need me, just rap on the wall."

The Sister walked to the wall and pounded on it.

"Like this," she said with a smile.

For the first time since entering the facility, Mary began to relax a little.

"Thank you, Sister," Mary replied with a smile.

Sister Gabriel is friendly, pretty, and has a vibrant personality, Mary silently noted. *Perhaps this is the creation of a warm and true friendship.*

But, moments later, the Sister left the room, and Mary once again felt cold and alone.

I must be careful, she silently chastised herself. *I must guard myself against exposing the truth. And a close friendship could easily weaken my vow of silence.*

Suddenly she felt the baby kick within her, and she gently placed her hand on the movement.

If my baby is a boy, I could unintentionally set his life up for danger before he is even born! No, she mused. *I must not feel close to anyone here. Even Sister Gabriel, who seems so kind and nice. I must be strong and hold our friendship at bay!*

Thus for the time being, Mary tried to distance herself as much as she reasonably could from everyone at the school. Nuns and students alike tried time after time to draw her into their inner circle, accepting her as a significant element in their daily lives. But with each attempt, Mary withdrew. She became paranoid, fearing that each act of friendship was merely a deviant bid to harm her and the baby.

She did not respond when the school newspaper added a bulletin of welcome to her.

"A young girl, like a flower, came to us today," the item stated. "She can write sentences on the blackboard."

Indeed, Mary's mastery of the written word was inconceivable to her hearing impaired peers. Previous scholastic training had encompassed a wide range of education!

In spite of self-denial, days passed quickly for Mary. Daylight hours were filled with instruction on hand-signing and lip-reading. Each day she learned more on the art of living a full and productive life with an inoperative audible sense.

One afternoon, class was dismissed by the Nun, but Mary did not leave the room with the other students. Although textbooks were stacked neatly on top of the desk, she did not move from her seat.

Perhaps I now know the reason for my loss of hearing, she thought as she gazed through the window of the classroom. *I was forced to take a vow of silence regarding my wonderful life in Vienna. Emperor Franz Josef demands that I be banished from history because of the love that Rudolph and I shared. And now, I must never speak of him ever again!*

Suddenly Mary's attention focused on a cardinal that had landed on a tree branch nearby. His beak opened, and his bright red breast quivered with the force of sound. The scene, void of nature's symphony, was unfamiliar to the deaf girl, and she laughed. Her impromptu burst of laughter frightened the bird, and he soared upward. She stood up and watched until the colorful bird disappeared from view.

She sighed and sat back down at her desk.

My time at the school has taught me more than the faculty will ever know, she silently decided. *I had forgotten that others can hear me, even though I cannot hear myself. Perhaps my loss of hearing is a blessing from God! If I never speak again, there will be no chance of error regarding my vow to Austrian nobility. Speech flows from one's mouth without effort, but signing requires time and forethought. And I, Baroness Mary Vetsera, true love of Crown Prince Rudolph, have been granted a blessing in deafness.*

Mary slowly stood to her feet and raised her right hand.

I will not utter another word for the rest of my life, she vowed.

After a moment, she smiled and picked up her books. While passing into the hallway, Sister Gabriel tapped her lightly on the shoulder, and she turned around to face the smiling Nun.

"Are you all right?" Sister Gabriel inquired with her hands.

Mary nodded politely.

The young Baroness felt like whistling as she walked to her room. She felt as though a heavy burden of worry had been suddenly lifted from her shoulders.

A vow of silence is a vow of complete *silence*, she mentally declared as she entered her room and closed the door. *And now I can start living again!*

After dinner that evening, Mary returned to her room and sat down at her desk. She removed a pen and a tablet of paper from the drawer.

For the first time, I feel that I will be able to write a fitting letter to my family. I miss them very much, and they do not even know it. The time has come for them to read of my life at the school and my love for them.

The first letter was to her parents. "My dearest John and Frances," she wrote.

She paused and put her pen on the desk and picked up the tablet. "Dear John and Frances," she read.

"That looks funny," Mary said with a giggle. Then remembering her vow, she quickly put her hand over her mouth and laid the tablet back down on the desk.

Twenty minutes later, she carefully folded two full sheets and slipped them into an envelope.

At least they will know I think of them often and love them very much. They will also have a better understanding of my new adventure at the Austin School for the Deaf. I hope they respond soon!

She picked up the pen once more and wrote, "Dearest Countess Marie."

Then she leaned back in her chair and gently tapped the end of the pen on the tablet. *I really should not use her title*, she thought, *but I am going to!*

As the pen glided over the paper, Mary smiled.

I have not forgotten your wonderful advice. I try to think of the many happy intervals from my past, and this has enabled me to push the bad memories from my present. This glimpse into happiness has spawned visions of my early years at the convent. The Nuns were so good to me, and I learned a lot during my time there. It was so peaceful and pleasant that I even considered becoming a Nun myself.

Bedtime here is really quite early. The nights get so long before I fall asleep. Every night I sit by my small desk remembering days past. In passing the time away, I have decided to write my memoirs, omitting the bad ones and writing only the happy ones.

Last night I was thinking about the time that you and I first attended the races at Badan. My uncles were in favor of my attendance since I had just then turned sixteen-years-old. They had finally agreed that I was old enough to be seen with the more mature. Then later, when we went to the next race at Freudenau, I met Rudi near the Danube for the first time. I believe that our destiny was set with love at first sight. I shall never forget Rudi and I dancing at Queen Victoria's 1887 Jubilee!

By this time, Rudi and I had acquired the greatest of respect for each other, he for my youth and I for his crown. Our togetherness brought us great joy, for we enjoyed doing the same things, even though they had to be done on the sly. I will never forget when Mama heard about Rudi and me through her brothers who found out through the Prince of Wales. I really thought that would be the beginning of the end. But Mama, on the contrary, felt that my friendship with the Crown Prince was an honor. And all too soon, every eyebrow became raised in suspicion as you and I attended every possible function that involved Rudolph.

My dear friend Countess, do you recall the numerous operas that we attended in hopes of seeing Rudi? And ice skating the wrong way around the rink to capture his attention? And the horseback ride in the park when Rudolph ordered his driver to stop? We did appear quite refined in our riding habits astride those beautiful Arabian horses, don't you agree?

I shall never forget Grinsing, Countess Marie. Dressed as Gypsies, you, Rudi, and I mingled with the crowd and danced and sang and laughed. Remember how you laughed at my long earrings dangling against my shoulders? And I will never forget the tambourine you had bought and tried to play. I do believe you did better with the castanets. And Rudi—how carried away he got with our exposed shoulders after a few wines. Thank God he knew which one he was talking to when he confessed his love. "Oh come, Rudi," I had said, "don't make a fool of yourself. And here, give me that glass of wine. Surely you don't need any more." I remember as well a few chosen words of your own you had for your cousin. Rudi finally responded, "Tonight we are Gypsies, and all Gypsies are happy and carefree!" The recollection of that enchanted night continues to delight me.

Mary slowly leaned back in her chair. For a moment, she basked within the lighthearted love and laughter of yesterday. Then with a shake of her head and a sad smile, the girl returned to the correspondence at hand.

And the night that we met Rudolph's train during the blizzard now warms my heart. He was returning from a relative's birthday celebration. You and I were so terri-

> bly cold—frozen to the bone. We sat in our carriage bundled and huddled together ever so closely. We kept our commitment, however, for you had promised your cousin that you would have me there. I can still hear the throb of the train engine as it stopped in front of the station. I felt that my heart was beating as loud as the clattering wheels against the steel rails. He looked so handsome, walking through the snowfall. Running toward him, I felt that my heart would burst with adoration! Our embrace and his passionate kiss were brief, but the memory will live forever.

Suddenly Mary felt the vibration of a loud knock on the door and slipped the tablet into her desk drawer. She stood up and greeted Sister Gabriel. The Nun smiled and handed her a small tray of cookies and a glass of milk. Mary set the cookies and milk on the desk.

"Thank you," Mary signed.

"You are welcome," Sister Gabriel replied.

The Nun over-compensated the lip movement, and Mary smiled her acknowledgment.

"Good night, Mary," Sister Gabriel signed. "Sleep well."

"Yes," Mary responded with her hands. "You also."

After the Nun had slipped back through the door and closed it, Mary retrieved the tablet from the desk drawer and picked up the pen.

> I sit here tonight, eating a cookie that Sister Gabriel brought, but my mind is taken back to the wonderful meals that you and I shared at the Grand Hotel in Vienna. Rudi asked us to join him on numerous occasions as he sat alone at a table. And then, as though by accident, he joined us later in your suite. Each time, you would have a glass of wine waiting for him, as if you knew all along he would be coming.

And the time we scoured the rooftops of the Hofburg Castle as we neared Rudi's quarters certainly added to the excitement of us two giggly women. Although the meeting between us was of a serious nature, sneaking through dark scary passageways lent an aura of intrigue. Thank God the right person was sent out to escort us in properly, or we should still be there trying to find our way.

So now I must thank you even at this late date for the love Rudolph and I shared. Your title should be "Precious Lady," Marie, for indeed you are and always will be a very special part of my life.

Please save this letter for me, for one day I may have need to see it again. I must close now. God be with you.

Mary quickly signed and folded the letter. After putting it in a separate envelope and sealing it, she put the pen and tablet away for the night. She quickly undressed and slipped between the sheets of the small bed. Although never to be the adoring Princess of the Crown Prince Rudolph, on this night Mary felt no pain nor remorse. For, within the darkness of the night, splendid visions of tender and elegant love enshrouded her with bliss. Amid the precious dreams, she gazed into her Rudolph's eyes and felt the warmth of his touch as he embraced her. And thus, for a brief moment, the princess, one who could never be, was indeed the most noble of all royalty.

NINETEEN

ALTHOUGH THE TREES ON THE VECERA ESTATE WERE NATURE'S method for cooling the long summer days, Countess Marie felt stifled by the warmth. She and Frances worked in the garden until the heat and humidity forced them to seek relief on the veranda. The Empress sat down in her rocking chair and fanned her perspiring brow, while Marie went to the kitchen for some lemonade.

Suddenly the rhythmic beat of horse's hooves on the road summoned Marie, Frances, and Annie to the front steps. A moment later, a horse and rider skidded to a halt at the hitching post.

"John!" Frances exclaimed. "Your horse is lathered with sweat! Are you all right?"

"Perfect!" he yelled.

He quickly slid from the saddle, waving a bundle of mail in one hand. In a lumbering trot, he hurried toward them.

"I am just perfect," he breathlessly repeated. "We received two letters from Mary today."

"Thank God," Frances whispered.

John handed a letter to Frances, and then he turned to Marie.

"This one is for you," he smiled.

"Thank you, John," she said. "It seems that she has been away for a year, rather than two months."

She glanced at the familiar scribe on the envelope before excusing herself.

She picked up her liquid refreshment and walked slowly into the house.

"John, would you care for something cool to drink?" Annie inquired.

"Yes, that sounds wonderful, Annie. Thank you," he replied.

As Marie entered the house and ascended the stairs, the voices from the veranda faded in the distance. The warmth of the day was forgotten while Marie absorbed every precious word. She smiled with each pleasant recollection. A powerful sense of gratitude engulfed her when she read of the dissipating nightmares.

After the third perusal of the letter, Marie carefully folded and replaced it in the envelope.

I will *keep this for Mary to read later*, she decided. *Perhaps one day she will need to be reminded again of the wonderful moments that we shared in the past.*

Marie put the envelope in her bureau drawer before again joining the others on the veranda.

"Marie," John said "I was just telling Frances that I hired a tutor for us. He is coming from Austin and should arrive early next week. With Mary due home in a couple of months, we need a greater understanding of her world of silence. He is going to instruct us in hand signing."

"That is a wonderful idea, John," Marie agreed.

That evening, dinner was a festive occasion. For the first time since Mary's departure, the home was filled with relaxed conversation and laughter. Annie prepared an exquisite meal and adorned the table with fresh flowers. Throughout the evening, lighthearted quips from Mary's letters added a special accent to the discussion. Later, Annie served coffee to John, Frances, and Marie on the veranda. A slight breeze rustled the leaves on the trees, creating a mental and physical reprieve from the heat. The melancholy call of a night bird greeted the arrival of the full moon that was ascending above the horizon. Indeed, the world seemed at peace as they sipped their coffee and listened to the sweet sound of nature.

"I feel as though Mary joined us this evening," Frances said quietly.

The comment was duly accepted with murmurs of agreement. Marie stood up and stretched.

"Good night, everyone," she smiled. "It has been a delightful evening, and I would rather not mar it by falling asleep on the veranda."

The Countess yawned as she entered her bedroom. When she opened her bureau drawer to remove a nightgown, Mary's letter slipped out and fell on the floor.

"Are you trying to tell me something, Mary?" she said with a giggle. "Okay. I believe that I am sufficiently awake to begin a letter to you."

Minutes later, the Countess was seated at her writing desk with pen in hand. "Dear Mary," she wrote:

> I am deeply touched by your written words. Thank you for sharing the memories with me. Your words have revived latent images in my mind.

Marie leaned back in her chair, savoring the graceful beauty of Vienna for a moment before continuing.

> Your extravagant wardrobe consistently set the pace for Viennese fashion, but you were indeed a vision of loveliness on the night of the Polish Ball. Two months prior to the affair, I visited Baroness Vetsera. During a stroll through the garden, I pointed to a pale yellow rose and suggested that a silk gown of the same color be found for Hanna to wear at the Ball. She agreed, adding that your introduction to society would be of the customary white attire.

Marie sighed as she summoned the pleasant recollection.

I shall never forget the introduction and entrance of Mary Alexandrine Vetsera that evening. Although a mere sixteen-year-old, your poise, beauty, and dignity exhibited the grace of one much more mature. You looked elegant in your white gown, and your dark hair was stylishly adorned with that crescent diamond heirloom. Your appearance cast an ambience of admiration amid those in attendance. With Stephanie bearing witness, Crown Prince Rudolph whisked you into the ballroom, and you and he danced the entire evening. The bond between you and Rudi was obvious as you gazed into one another's eyes. Yes, dear Mary, you were indeed the perfect Princess at the Polish Ball. The ladies were in awe as they brought up their fans to their faces. Snickering gossip spread like wildfire. The following day, all of Vienna had heard and marveled about their crown prince and his new fairy princess.

Marie paused and put her pen down. She reached for her handkerchief and dried the tears from her cheeks. She then cleared her throat and retrieved the pen.

Soon after that memorable evening, Baroness Vetsera informally assigned me as your chaperon. Although I was much older, your vitality and love of life was an inspiration for me. We frequently entertained Vetsera visitors—you playing the piano, while I accompanied you with the zither. We were natural entertainers, unless Chopin or Mozart was requested!

Marie laughed with the recollection.

I met Baroness Vetsera for the first time at the estate of Count Eszterhazy at Godollo. She was there to visit with her brothers Aristide and Hector, who were house guests of the Count. She and I became truly good friends during this time. When she decided to relocate to Vienna, I assisted with the guest list for her introductory ball. She was not astonished by the titled nobility invited. The Prince of Wales, Prince Edward, the Duke of Braganza of Portugal, Count Stockau, Countess St. Julian, and Count Eszterhazy were among those in attendance. The gala affair also included Kathrina Schratt, an actress who was also the mistress of the Emperor, diplomats, statesmen, physicians, professors, and myself, the Countess of Bavaria.

The Vetsera - Baltazzi Ball was a memorable and elegant evening. Carriages had lined the sweeping, tree-lined driveway to the mansion. The walkway had massive urns of baby roses and azaleas, each pot arranged to such perfection that it could have been a photograph. Your guests had been escorted beyond the French doors at the end of the hall. Cocktails were served in the elegant terrace that was softly aglow with green and blue lights. The fountains in the garden surrounding the gazebo seemed to have danced in unison to the music of Mozart, Hayden, and Bach played by the chamber musicians.

The ladies had carefully observed which hors d'oeuvre to choose and the gentlemen observed the ladies as they sparkled under the massive crystal chandelier. As the music began in the ballroom, the ladies impatiently waited for their handsome partners and for the dance to begin.

The beauty and poise of you and your sister Hanna were comparable with that of Baroness Helene Vetsera. I remember you two standing along side of your mother. The proud and elegant Baroness had greeted her guests with anticipation as they entered the vast marble-floored

> hall. Even among the galaxy of bejeweled society, the three of you baronesses had dazzled and outshone your guests.
>
> Mary, she was so pleased when you and the Duke of Braganza entered the ballroom and danced. She had high expectations of the two of you marrying one day. This union was not to be, of course, for your destiny was woven within the love of the Crown Prince of Austria.

Marie ended the letter, closing with "Sweet dreams, Princess," then turned back the bed covers and settled between the sheets.

"The tutor from the Austin School for the Deaf will soon be arriving," she murmured sleepily, "re-uniting the five of us with a learned and loving bond of inaudible communication. I look forward to the alliance and the challenge."

The pillow felt cool against her face. She smiled and closed her eyes in peaceful slumber.

For the first time in several months, the Vecera family rested within a tenor of serenity. Each member felt contented, knowing that Mary would soon be an inherent part of their lives once again.

Two days prior to Mary's departure from the school, John and Mr. Brown, a hired hand, made the trip to Austin. John felt his heartbeat quicken as he reined the team to a halt in front of the school and handed the reins to Mr. Brown.

"I should not be long, Mr. Brown," he said. "You stay with the team and wagon while I get Mary and her belongings."

"Yes Sir, Boss," the hired hand responded. "I will be waiting right here."

The Mother Superior was expecting Mary's father, and therefore, John was immediately ushered into her office.

"I am a bit concerned about Mary making the long journey to Muldoon at this time, Mr. Vecera," the Mother Superior stated. "She has not been feeling well for several days now."

John smiled and said, "I appreciate your regard for her well being, Mother Superior, but she will be fine."

He stood up to leave.

"Thank you for taking such good care of her. I hope that you will consider accepting her back into the school after her baby is born."

"Yes. Most certainly," Mr. Vecera. We will look forward to her return," Mother Superior agreed. "She has been a joy. She was somewhat timid at first, but she seems to have overcome that obstacle and has made so many good friends here. They will miss her terribly."

The Mother Superior hesitated for a moment.

"As a matter of fact, Mr. Vecera, two Nuns from Austria recently transferred to our school. They have become very close to Mary, almost insisting that she remain here for the birth of her child." Then she added proudly, "It is true that we have a fine physician on the premises who is perfectly capable of handling of the situation."

John suddenly felt that his blood had turned to ice. He struggled to regain his composure before replying.

"I am quite sure that your physician is beyond reproach, Mother Superior, but we feel that Mary should be with her family at this time."

He cleared his throat before inquiring, "Do many Sisters from other countries request transfer to Austin?"

"No," she replied thoughtfully. "No. Indeed, Mr. Vecera, it is quite unusual. Most of our inner faculty and staff are local."

John looked down at the hat that he was clutching in his hands. He walked from the door to the window beside her desk and stared at the grounds below. A moment later, he diverted his gaze to the Mother Superior. His face was flushed, and a bead of perspiration was visible on his brow.

"I am concerned for Mary's safety," he suddenly stated in a husky voice. "Just how much information do you have on the two Austrian Nuns?"

"I see," the Mother Superior said quietly. "Sit down a moment, Mr. Vecera, and we will retrieve their files."

As she walked to the door and opened it, John moved to the nearest chair and sat down.

"Sister Gabriel," the Mother Superior declared in a forceful tone. "Get me the files on the two Nuns from Austria. Please bring them into my office at once."

Soon, the files were on the desk of the Mother Superior. Sister Gabriel and John listened carefully as the administrator reviewed the information.

"They are both from the convent near Vienna," the Mother Superior said.

"Yes," John said grimly. "I have heard of this convent. It is well known throughout Austria for aborting illegitimate child bearing among the nobility."

He stood up and walked to the door.

"I must get Mary away from them at once."

"I agree," Mother Superior replied as she rose to her feet. "But, Mr. Vecera, her removal from the school will be safer if effected under the cover of darkness."

"Yes, of course," John agreed. "I will return for her at midnight."

"Very well," the Mother Superior responded. "We will have her waiting for you at the rear entrance at midnight. Good day, Mr. Vecera, and good luck on your return journey."

And thus, the rendezvous transpired beneath the light of the moon. As though reliving a portion from the past, the wagon thundered through the shadows, bearing cargo more precious than gold. But on this night, the flight from perilous Austrians occurred within the sanctity of Texas in a rig less ornate.

Mary smiled and leaned back against blankets in the wagon. They had long ago left the city of Austin, traversing in a southeasterly direction toward her home near Muldoon. She looked at her father, who was seated across from her, and smiled. He responded with a loving pat on her shoulder. She sighed contentedly and turned her attention to the ghostly myriad of trees along the road. The wagon moving through the veil of moonlight was soothing to the youthful deaf girl, and the miles pleasantly slipped behind them.

Suddenly, a sharp pain in her abdomen caused her to clutch the area and moan.

"Are you all right, Mary?" John signed. He was grateful for the moonlight. Otherwise it would have been very difficult to communicate.

"Yes, Papa," she replied with her hands. "I had a pain, but it is gone now."

"The baby is not due yet, is it?"

"No, Papa," Mary signed and smiled. "Not until the middle of September."

She saw him exhale in relief.

"Good," he said.

"Don't worry, Papa," she signed with a giggle. "We will be home long before . . ."

Again the pain seared through her, and she gasped.

"Oh no!" John bellowed. "Mr. Brown, please hurry to the nearest town."

Nearly thirty minutes later, Mary's intervals of pain had increased in length and intensity. John was rapidly approaching a state of panic.

"Mr. Brown," he yelled. "Forget the nearest town. Find the nearest house and stop!"

Soon, the wagon rolled to a halt in front of a farmhouse. John jumped out and ran to the door, while Mr. Brown tied the weary team to the hitching post.

Mary was quickly accepted and taken into a bedroom. The woman of the house began attending to her needs. John explained to the impromptu midwife about Mary's lack of verbal communication. He signed words of encouragement to Mary that were spoken by the kind woman until the two women felt comfortable with one another. Then he left the bedroom.

John did not hear many cries, for Mary had accepted her pain with grace. Her thoughts became happy ones, framed around the fact that nine months of stress was ending. She then suddenly wished she was back in Vienna, going through her armoire of gorgeous slim gowns, and even welcoming her corsets that would at the moment make for a rather tight fit.

Throughout the remainder of the night and into the following morning, John waited in the kitchen with the other men. About mid-morning, they heard a baby cry. And only minutes later, the midwife entered the kitchen.

"Mr. Vecera, you have a beautiful baby granddaughter!" she announced proudly. "She and her mother are waiting to see you."

The news sent John scurrying back into the bedroom. He stopped beside the bed and stared at the little bundle in Mary's arms.

"She is beautiful!" he whispered.

He gently touched the tiny girl on her cheek, and she wriggled in Mary's arms. John laughed and leaned over and kissed Mary on her forehead. He then stepped back from the bed and quickly signed his feelings to Mary. She smiled and nodded.

"What are you going to name her?" he asked.

"J-u-l-i-a-n-n-a," Mary quickly spelled in sign. "But we will call her J-u-l-i-a."

Mary carefully studied her father's lip movement as he spoke the baby's name. Then she reached out with Julia for him to hold. He sat down on the chair beside the bed with the little bundle in his arms. He studied each tiny little finger and gazed at her face as though memorizing each minute detail.

Several minutes later, he handed the child back to Mary and kissed her again before leaving the room.

The remainder of the journey to the Vecera Estate was made without interruption. Mary lovingly held Julia in her arms as the miles passed beneath them. With each awakening of the infant, Mary smiled. The babe yawned, stretched, and wriggled each time.

Rudolph would be so proud of you, my daughter, she thought. *As I look at you, I feel that he is with us. You would have been very proud of him, my baby Julianna. Very proud indeed.*

As the babe settled into a deep sleep once again, Mary turned her attention to the countryside. Suddenly her heart began to beat faster, and she tapped her father on the arm and pointed. He smiled and nodded. Mary then looked down at the baby in her arms.

We are home, Julia. We are on the lane that leads to our house right now, she silently informed the child.

She waved as Frances, Marie, and Annie ran down the steps toward them. They gathered near the wagon as it stopped in front of the house. The Empress expressed surprise, immediately followed by elation when she noticed the little bundle in the arms of her daughter. The matron carefully picked up the infant while Marie and Annie helped Mary from the rig.

"My daughter's name is J-u-l-i-a-n-n-a," Mary quickly signed. "We will call her J-u-l-i-a."

"Julia is beautiful," the Countess responded with her hands.

As Frances accepted her granddaughter, she declared, "Now the curse of the past nine months has ended. The spies that have watched so dutifully can now return to Vienna triumphant, and report to the Emperor that no more bloodshed will be needed, that his kingdom is safe."

That night, while lying in her own bed with her daughter sleeping peacefully beside her, Mary felt at peace with the world. For the first time, she fully comprehended the pain behind her mother's decision so many years earlier when *she* was born and given away.

Mary looked deeply into her newborn's eyes and silently resolved, *No, no, I could never do the same.*

How frightened my mother must have been, Mary then mused. *I am truly grateful that she gave me to Baroness Vetsera and Papa.*

She gazed at her daughter, absorbing and savoring the precious gift from God.

I now understand the protective love of a mother for her child. I love you, my baby Julia. I truly do. Your father loved you too, and you need to be told of your heritage one day. You, Julianna, will know of your father, for you shall hear his name!

Thus the night passed with Mary alert to every need of her baby. The Vecera family was once again united, and the burden of a possible Austrian assault on an heir to the throne was cast into the shadow of times past.

With the arrival of Julia, a beacon of hope was seemingly implanted within the hearts of the exiled. And indeed, their lives appeared bright and youthful upon the horizon of tomorrow.

TWENTY

FROM THE MOMENT OF HER ARRIVAL, JULIA CAPTURED THE heart and attention of everyone at the Vecera Estate. Her presence added life and purpose, and thus each day was a new adventure. As the weeks sped by, daily conversations became narratives on the gurgles, coos, and smiles of the child.

Three months later, however, preparations began for Mary's return trip to school. Annie spent many hours at the pedal sewing machine, designing and sewing dresses for Mary to take with her. While Frances and Marie shopped for new underclothing and a nice winter coat, John bought new combs and a ribbon for her hair.

Late one evening, a team and wagon suddenly appeared among the trees and approached the Vecera home. Annie nervously opened the door and stepped onto the veranda. The team halted in front of the house, and a large man stepped down.

As he slowly walked toward the house, Frances, Marie, and Mary joined Annie on the porch.

Suddenly Marie recognized the stranger and she became horrified.

"Bradfisch!" she gasped. "It is Bradfisch."

The four women screamed and quickly ran inside the house.

Oh, he's come to kill me and my baby, Mary thought as she dashed upstairs in panic. She hurriedly wrapped Julia in a blanket, and cradled her tightly in the corner of a closet.

The Countess hurried to the study and jerked the shotgun from the pegs on the wall. With gun in hand, she ran back to the front door and stepped onto the veranda. Then with her feet planted on the edge of the first step, she aimed the barrel at the man's chest.

"If you have a weapon, drop it!" she demanded. "Now!"

Bradfisch pulled the right side of his coat back, exposing a pistol.

"Slowly!" Marie shrieked. "And drop it!"

With a precise motion, he carefully extracted the gun from the holster and let it fall to the ground.

"Go away!" the Empress interjected in a loud voice. "Go away and leave us alone. You are not welcome here!"

"Please," Bradfisch said as he raised his hands above his head. "You must hear me out. I am not here to harm you. I only want to know if Mary is all right. And I am here to beg forgiveness from all of you."

Marie did not lower nor reposition the aim of the shotgun.

"Please understand," he begged. "I cannot continue this way. I was forced to do it. The Emperor threatened my family! Each of you know that I loved the Crown Prince. I was his dedicated servant."

He looked first at Marie and then at Frances and Annie who were now standing in the doorway. Tears streamed down his face as the three women silently stared at him with hate.

He slowly lowered his arms and turned around. His shoulders slumped in defeat as he walked toward the sweating team of horses. He felt dejected, defeated. It was obvious he was to receive neither sympathy nor forgiveness. He would have to go—where he was not sure, and where he did not care.

He stepped up on the wagon and gathered the lines in his hands. Without a backward glance, the former Vienna cabby gently snapped the lines against the rumps of the tired horses. The wagon creaked and groaned as though mourning for the defeated man aboard.

Suddenly John appeared at the bottom of the steps. He was holding his rifle limply in one hand as he looked up at the Vecera women on the veranda.

"He is a broken man," John said. "I overheard the conversation, and I feel that we should hear his explanation." His gaze shifted to the departing rig.

"Bradfisch looks tired and hungry. I think we should call him back."

The Empress finally gave a hesitant nod, and John trotted down the lane after the exhausted team and driver.

Moments later, John returned with Bradfisch. The two men unhitched, fed, and watered the team before entering the house.

"Where is Mary?" John asked as he motioned for Bradfisch to be seated.

"Annie found her hidden in the closet," Marie replied.

"Is she all right?"

"Yes. She has calmed down now, and she is resting comfortably."

"Good," John responded. "Annie, would you kindly prepare something for Bradfisch to eat? I doubt that he has strength enough at the moment to tell us his side of the story."

They filled the time with small talk until Annie returned with some nourishment. After eating ravenously, Bradfisch leaned back in his chair and complemented Annie on her fine cooking skills.

"Did the Emperor exile you from Austria?" John asked.

"The order came from Count Taaffe, but I am quite sure that the decree originated from Emperor Franz Josef," Bradfisch said. "I was handed an envelope, and the message stated that it would be to my best interest to leave the country immediately."

After taking a sip of coffee, the cabby said, "I tried to drown the heartache from my soul with liquor. Unfortunately, the whiskey did nothing whatsoever to ease the awful pain in my heart."

He paused and looked at John.

"Soon I, too, was put aboard a ship to America. I felt very alone and sick about having to leave my family in Austria. The ship finally docked, but my mental state had deteriorated even more during the voyage. Nightmares and ocean sickness had drained me of determination and stolen my moments for preparation. And yet one day, I found myself walking down the dock in New York with a new name, Ben Freidrich, in a strange country without a destination in mind."

"It must have been frightening," Frances murmured.

"Yes," Bradfisch agreed. "Indeed, for the first time in my life, I felt trapped , There was no reason for living. Instinctively, I found a job as a cabby, which made the days pass quickly. But, during off hours, I again found solace in whiskey, frequenting the New York pubs. With a small, dreary room for a home and my money pouring into local pubs, I was unable to receive any peace."

Ben looked at each person present as though silently pleading for grace.

"By now I was in a desperate way. I could not eat nor sleep. Nightmares of never seeing my family again kept haunting me. I thought I would die, in fact I wanted to die. Then, one day, I faced the truth. By forgiving me, you are the only ones who can now grant me an honorable and worthwhile life."

"How did you find us?" John asked.

Ben paused a moment before replying, "I have friends who are on the police force in Vienna. I contacted them, and they were kind enough to share information regarding the destination of Mary's ship. I left New York and took the shortest route to the Gulf of Mexico. Then, following the coastline, I finally arrived in Galveston. Upon my arrival, the Harbor Master mentioned the town of LaGrange, casually remarking that many Europeans had settled in that area. From there I was finally directed to Muldoon. As I proceeded, I was constantly reminded of things I wanted to forget. This way of life was certainly a contrast to my happy life in Vienna. There I whistled and sang for Rudolph. Now there would be no more whistling; the songs had ended."

Suddenly Ben's voice grew faint, and he closed his eyes for a moment.

"In LaGrange, I tried to locate you without leaving suspicions among the people. By this time, I was so mentally and physically exhausted that I . . ."

His voice trailed off into silence. The song of crickets echoed against the stillness of the night as the small band waited, but Ben did not finish his sentence.

Finally the Empress spoke.

"We Vecera's have promised one another that the past cannot be changed nor polished by grief," she declared in a firm tone. "We must all begin life anew!"

Marie covered her mouth with one hand, trying to hide a faint smile.

Empress Elizabeth has returned, the Countess thought. *In the style and grace of a Royal Order, she is insisting that we build hope and optimism into our future. Thank you, dear Empress Elizabeth.*

Suddenly Marie heard Julia cry, and she glanced toward the source. Mary was standing on the landing at the top of the stairs with the baby in her arms. Bradfisch followed her gaze to the mother and gasped.

"A baby?" he whispered hoarsely. He stood up and walked slowly toward the staircase as Mary descended.

"You have a baby?" he murmured. "Thank God, you are all right!"

He moved a step closer to the bannister, but Mary stepped back. Marie started to stand up, but John and Frances both motioned for her to remain seated.

The victim and assassin stared at one another for a long moment, but Ben did not attempt to move closer. Seconds later, Mary stepped off the landing and moved down the stairs toward him. He did not speak as she stepped onto the main floor. After a long pause, the assassin of the Crown Prince, slowly extended his hands to take the princess, and Mary gently placed Julia in his arms.

They all stood in silence for a moment as Bradfisch observed the baby from head to toe. He looked frozen in disbelief.

"Oh, Dear God," he said. "I did not know that you were with child, Mary."

Empress Elizabeth, Baron Vetsera, Countess Larisch, Baroness Mary Vetsera, and Austrian maid Agnes bore witness as Bradfisch gazed down upon the sweet face of Rudolph and Mary's daughter.

Gratefulness was an inadequate feeling to describe what he felt for, not one, but two lives that had been spared that miraculous day in Mayerling.

"Oh Dear God, thank You for sparing this mother and child," he prayed, as tears streamed down his face.

TWENTY-ONE

THE NOVEMBER EVENING WAS PLEASANT IN TEMPERATURE AS the Austrian exiles gathered on the veranda. After everyone was comfortably seated, Ben Freidrich pulled a cheroot from his vest pocket. He stared at it for a moment before striking a match and lighting it.

"Rudolph had become involved with Frances Marie Kaspar, nicknamed Mitzi by Rudolph," He quietly said. "This promiscuous affair began prior to meeting you, Mary."

The Countess signed the message to Mary, but the girl had already received the words by lip reading.

"One evening, the Crown Prince went to Mitzi in a state of inebriation. He told the mistress that he was in love with Mary, and she would one day be his Queen of Hungary. This infuriated Mitzi. She later told her attorney of Rudolph's plan, and he advised her to sell the information to Emperor Franz Josef. And so the Prince was set up."

Whispers of surprise swept through the assemblage. Ben snubbed out the cigar and drew a deep breath.

"Within a short time, *I* was the one ordered by the Emperor to assassinate both Rudolph and Mary, creating a portrayal of double suicide. If I cooperated, my family would receive substantial financial gain. But if I refused . . ."

Ben paused and looked at Mary.

"If I refused, my family would suffer bodily harm. I could not believe this was happening to me, even though I understood why *I* was picked. I was the only one who could get close enough to them without creating suspicion. But I did not want the financial security they so politely promised. Yet there was nothing I could do. I was half frozen with fear, yet I had to get control of myself in order to carry out this awesome task ahead of me. My orders from the highest court were not to carry Rudolph to Mayerling that weekend as I had always done. Loschak, Rudolph's valet would have the honor instead. I was to pretend being ill and remain home until the next day. I truly *did* feel sick when Mary arrived for the journey to Mayerling that morning.

"Normally a trip to the lodge was a pleasure, but this one was a nightmare! In fact, it turned out to be the worst day of my life. Oh, how many times I wanted to ride in the opposite direction. But it was too late, for I sensed that I was being spied upon. I was trapped. As I looked around me, I saw deer rummaging through the snow for something to eat. They appeared so pure and innocent. I wondered how anyone would even want to end *their* lives. When I glanced back at Mary, she looked as peaceful as the deer. I wondered how anyone would want this innocent and beautiful girl to come to harm."

Ben shook his head as though trying to erase the scene from his mind.

"As per orders, I delivered Mary to the lodge. I watched her run through the gate toward the Crown Prince. He could see the top of the carriage outside the walled encampment as I moved it forward, then again reined the team to a halt beside the tea house. By that time I had jumped down from the carriage and aimed the pistol at them through the tea house windows. Rudolph, already justifiably suspicious of my actions, had grabbed Mary and tried to push her to safety inside of his private quarters. But it was too late. I had already begun to fire.

"For a small eternity I closed my eyes. Then I hurriedly began moving toward the building. My hope was that maybe I had missed. Unfortunately, they were both lying upon the snow in a pool of blood. Their hands were touching, but both appeared to be dead. Portions of Rudolph's skull and brains were strewn about the area. I then made the tragedy seem a double suicide by placing the pistol between the still forms. Horrified and sickened by the sight, I backed away from them and fell in the snow. All I could do was weep and rock back and forth in the blue cold of dusk."

Frances rose to her feet and walked over to Ben. She glanced at him before moving to the bannister and staring into the darkness of the night.

"It appears that you had no choice," she murmured. "The Emperor demanded the assassinations."

Ben nodded and cleared his throat before recommencing.

"Presently the servants made their appearance and the panic began. One sobbed heavily. Another muttered, 'This cannot be so. Not our Crown Prince.' Most stood stiffly in horror as they made the sign of the cross and prayed.

"Soon, Count Hoyos and Prince Phillip of Coburg arrived at my side. They shook me and asked, 'For God's sake what has happened?' At first, I could not utter a sound. Then I told them that I had not seen the tragedy occur. We hurriedly carried Rudolph into his bedroom and returned for Mary. To our surprise, she was still alive, so we carried her into the woodshed until the authorities could offer further directions. Soon the lodge was converged upon by officials. Some of those in attendance included: Count Taaffe, Baron Krauss, Chief Commissioner Wyspouzill, Medical Examiner Slatin, Chief of Protocol Baron Gorup, Court Reporter Hofrat Kubasek, Court Physician Dr. Auchenthaler, Officer Kubachek, Officer Habrada, plus other detectives and officials.

"I was fearful for both my family and myself while we awaited the word that I had dared not even hope for—that Mary would indeed survive. And since Mary's survival certainly wasn't on the planned agenda, I knew Count Von Taaffe would have to think quickly. I wondered what he would do with Mary Vetsera alive and a witness to the assassination. I was so frightened I considered running, but I knew that hiding would be to no avail."

"That is true," John agreed. "How did Count Taaffe handle the cover up?"

"Sometime later I learned that a mock burial had been held," Ben said quietly, "and as far as everyone was concerned, Mary Alexandrine Vetsera was buried in the cemetery of Heilingenkreuz."

"Yes," Frances said. "I was all too aware that they were planning to fabricate her death."

Mary looked at Marie. The Countess quickly signed confirmation of her burial. Mary nodded and turned her attention back to Ben.

"Baron Krauss went with Mary and her uncles to the ancient abbey of Heilingenkreuz," the cabby continued. "When Abbot Grunbock refused to bury an empty coffin to represent the death of Baroness Mary, Baron Krauss explained that he had no choice. The mock burial was a direct order from the Emperor. The ground was frozen, but the grave diggers were finally able to accomplish their bizarre task by the early morning hours. And so the empty wooden box was all to attest that Mary Vetsera was indeed dead and buried."

"And Rudolph?" John asked. "How did the authorities handle his arrangements?"

Ben slowly shook his head and sighed.

"His body was placed in a fourgon pulled by two black horses. He was taken to Vienna for burial in the Capuchine Vault."

He looked at Countess Marie for a moment before continuing.

"It is strange that I was his cabby and close friend for so many years, and yet I was destined to be his assassin, standing by as he took his final ride."

Marie walked to the bannister and stood beside Frances.

"You were also a victim, Ben," she said softly. "You only acted under the orders of the Emperor."

"Why were you asked to leave?" John inquired. "It sounds as though the deception was completely successful."

"Soon after the burial of the Crown Prince, rumors began to spread. The authorities were getting different stories from the servants, and the public was demanding that the truth be told. And, I, among others, became a threat. I am afraid they quickly realized the large doses of whiskey only served to loosen my tongue. I was issued a new identity and exiled."

Ben slowly stood to his feet. His face was pallid, and his hands trembled from the remembrance.

"Now you know the truth," he said quietly. "It is time for me to go now. I hope that you will one day be able to forgive me."

With the posture of a beaten man, he walked slowly toward the front steps.

"Wait!" Frances said.

She walked to him and put her hand on his shoulder.

"Marie is right. You are a victim."

The Empress waved her hand toward John, Marie, Mary, and Annie.

"We are all victims of the vicious Emperor," she said. "Please stay here with us. It seems only right that we remain together—at least for a while."

John stood up and walked to Ben. He extended his hand in a gesture of acceptance. The cabby cautiously put his hand in John's.

"Yes," John said. "I agree with Frances, Ben. You should stay with us. Give yourself a chance to formulate a plan for your future."

Ben looked at Marie, Mary, and Annie. All three smiled and nodded. He then clasped John's hand between both of his and firmly shook it.

"Yes," he said gratefully. "I appreciate your invitation very much."

Thus, Bradfisch, as Ben Freidrich, gratefully accepted—and for all practical purposes, became a member of the family. Needless to say, his somber dissertation on that winter evening would never be forgotten by the despaired household.

And thus, the lives of the exiled were united in a bond of friendship. Pain from the past eased with the healing salve of understanding as the Empress, Baron, Countess, Baroness, maid, and royal carriage driver entered the Vecera home and shut the door.

TWENTY-TWO

SOON AFTER THE ARRIVAL OF BRADFISCH, MARY RETURNED TO the School for the Deaf in Austin. She felt in tune with life as she walked up the familiar steps to the big double-doors.

The setting is so serene, she mused. *I wonder why I ever felt that the building looked like a prison. It certainly looks friendly now!*

As she opened the door, the Mother Superior was waiting to greet her. John had informed her when Mary would be arriving.

"Welcome back, Mary Vecera," she said. "We have been looking forward to your return."

Mary smiled and signed, "Thank you, Mother Superior. I, too, missed my friends at the school."

The Mother Superior held the Baroness at arms length.

"You look rested and very healthy. We were concerned about you on the night of your departure."

"I have lost weight," Mary signed with a grin, "and gained a beautiful baby girl."

"A baby girl. Mary, that is wonderful!" the Administrator said. "Now you must hurry to your room. You will need to freshen up before dinner."

Mary nodded and continued walking toward her quarters.

I wonder where Sister Gabriel is working, she pondered. *I had hoped that she and the others would be waiting for me.*

As the familiar door to her quarters swung open, a flurry of black and white habits converged upon her.

Sister Gabriel was the first to embrace her.

"I am so happy that you are back," she smiled. "We have all missed you. And," she added with a wink, "we have a surprise for you!"

Mary looked beyond the Sister. Suddenly her eyes sparkled with excitement, and her hands darted in a fit of rapid motion.

"Slow down," Sister Gabriel laughed. "I cannot read your message."

"You have painted my room," Mary slowly signed. "It looks so light and cheerful. Thank you, my friends."

Mary embraced each one as they exited the small room, and then she turned to Sister Gabriel.

"I have missed you," she signed. "I feel that I have returned to my second home. But my heart is heavy for my baby daughter. I had to leave her with my family, but I so much wish that you could see her. She is beautiful!"

Sister Gabriel helped Mary unpack, asking a barrage of questions about baby Julia throughout the task. Mary proudly related each minute and wonderful detail about her new girl child.

"Julia is very tiny. She has big eyes, an oval face, and a lot of hair. She looks like her grandmother. She is healthy and truly beautiful. Everyone at home is overjoyed with her."

Suddenly, a tear trickled down Mary's cheek. Sister Gabriel embraced the young mother.

"And you miss her already?" the Sister asked.

"Yes," Mary signed before brushing the tear from her face. "I want to return to her as soon as possible."

"Of course. And you will, my friend," Sister Gabriel stressed with her hands. "Your time here will pass quickly, and then you can rejoin Julia. But for tonight, I want you to have dinner with me and the other Sisters. Okay?"

Mary nodded with a faint smile of appreciation.

"Yes," she signed. "I would enjoy that very much."

As the pair started toward the door, Mary suddenly stopped, signing, "Where are the two Sisters from . . ."

Sister Gabriel touched the girl's hands, stopping her in mid-sentence. She slowly shook her head and motioned for Mary to lead the way to the dining room.

The following morning, after a restful night of sleep and a hearty breakfast, Mary entered her classroom. She stopped and stared in surprise when she saw the message that was written on the blackboard.

"Mary, We love you. Welcome back, Teacher!"

The Baroness felt her face blush with excitement, and she looked about the room for the source of the note. Sister Gabriel was standing on the opposite side of the room. The Nun smiled and nodded.

"We all agree that you will make a fine teacher, Mary," she said as she approached the girl. "You have a wonderful rapport with the younger students, and we need you to work with them."

And thus during her second term, Mary Vecera began a new and rewarding adventure within the Austin School for the Deaf.

One afternoon, Mother Superior beckoned Mary into her office. The youthful teacher noticed that several city dignitaries were seated within the room as she entered.

"Mary, you have been chosen to represent the Austin School for the Deaf in the annual parade in Austin," the Mother Superior announced. "We concur that you are an inspiration for the hearing impaired and the city of Austin as well."

"I do not understand," Mary signed. "What do you want me to do?"

Mother Superior smiled and patted the teacher on her shoulder.

"On the day of the city's annual celebration, you will ride horseback down the main street of Austin."

The Mother Superior walked over to her desk and picked up a long, white piece of satin fabric. AUSTIN SCHOOL FOR THE DEAF was printed across the front of it in gold letters. She held it out for Mary to read.

"If you agree to represent us, Mary," the Sister smiled, "you will wear this as the procession slowly passes through the main section of the city. You will represent every administrator, teacher, and student here. I personally will be very proud and pleased if you accept the honor."

Mary glanced at each person in the room before slowly nodding her head.

"Thank you," the Mother Superior related as Mary hand signed her reply. "I will be pleased and honored to represent our school in the Annual Austin Parade."

Mary blushed slightly as she looked around the room and saw everyone standing and applauding her decision.

Sister Gabriel and four others were waiting for Mary as she left the office and entered the hallway.

"Congratulations!" the Sister signed before embracing the young Baroness. "We are all so proud that you will represent us. You are indeed a beautiful and regal representative for our school."

Thus, several weeks later, the honor was bestowed upon Mary. The banner was securely affixed across her bodice, and her long, dark hair glistened beneath the rays of the warm Texas sun. At one point along the parade route, Mary saw the Mother Superior seated amid numerous students and faculty members, and she acknowledged them with a smile and a wave. The Mother Superior immediately led the assemblage in a heartfelt round of applause for the school's thrilled representative. The poise and grace displayed atop the white prancing horse was a breathtaking portrait of nobility. Although truth of heritage lost in tarnished history, on this day, Princess Mary Alexandrine Vetsera indeed graced the celebration in Austin, Texas, with her proud and regal attendance.

TWENTY-THREE

IN THE SPRING OF 1892, JOHN VECERA AND BEN FREIDRICH traveled to Austin in the covered wagon. Mary was coming home for the first time in three years, and the former Baron was ecstatic. Although keeping abreast of Mary's life, the numerous pages of correspondence between Austin and Muldoon did not compensate for her absence.

"Three years, Ben," John said softly as the team approached the outskirts of the city. "Does it seem that Mary has been gone for three years?"

"No," Ben chuckled. "It does not seem feasible that I have been with you for that span of time either. But, Julia was a baby when she left, and now that little girl is a pretty and rambunctious three-year-old."

"True," John smiled. "Mary mentioned her respect and love for the students and her yearning and love for Julia in every letter. The turmoil of emotions has been hard on her. The reunion between my daughter and granddaughter should be a wonderful sight to behold."

"Yes, it will," Ben agreed.

He gently snapped the lines against the rumps of the horses as they started down the main street of Austin. The Texas capital was energetic and bustling with activity, so he matched the team's pace with the flow.

"Mr. Brown was telling me that the capital of the Republic of Texas was originally located in Houston," Ben commented.

"Yes, it was," John agreed. "Over half a century ago, the furniture and archives were moved to Austin. The transfer required fifty ox-drawn wagons."

"That would have been a sight to behold," Ben proclaimed. "America is a fascinating frontier."

"Indeed, it is," John chuckled. "There is little similarity between the United States and the monarchy of Austria."

Ben smiled and nodded as he reined the team to a halt in front of the school.

John entered the building and returned within a short time with Mary at his side. He assisted her aboard before stowing the baggage in the back of the wagon.

"It is quite obvious that my daughter will be missed at the school," John smiled. "After tearful farewells, everyone stressed that she would always have a post with the school."

Mary nodded and signed, "I told Sister Gabriel that I must see Julia soon. If I do not, the two of us shall forever be strangers!"

John smiled and said, "We will not allow that to happen, Mary. We will take you home at once."

Throughout the journey, the father and daughter communicated through hand signing and lip-reading. John had not forgotten that Mary had to watch him speak, so they faced one another as the miles passed beneath them.

As they rounded a curve in the road, John noted, "I have never spoken to you about my past, dear daughter. Perhaps this would be an excellent opportunity to do so."

Mary smiled her approval and signed, "I would love to hear about it, Papa."

"Very well," he began. "Perhaps I should begin with my father. His name was Bernard. As a young man, he taught Government in an Austrian University. His brother, Franz Vetsera, had degrees in both Theology and Philosophy. My father later became an Archeology professor at the National

Albert Museum, plus he held the position of director for the gymnasium in Pest. Our home was in Bratislava.

"Following the ambitious pattern set by my father and uncle, I began my pursuit for success at an early age. In 1849, at age thirty-two, I accepted a position on the Diplomatic Service of the Oriental Academy in Vienna. Soon, I was commissioned as Aide to the Austrian - Hungarian Embassy in Constantinople."

After relating numerous details of his life, John paused. But Mary's interest had now peaked and she nudged him on the shoulder.

"Please go on, Papa," she signed.

"I was just remembering a Turkish Ball that I once attended, Mary," he smiled. "The room was full of massive marble pillars, and a large silk cloth hung in waves in the ceiling. That was the night that I first met Helene. This was the beginning of my romance with the dark-haired beauty who would later became my wife. Our courtship encompassed visits to the Sultan's Almed's Mosque, the Hagia Sophia, and the Pyramid of Cheops, where Cleopatra once had a villa."

"How romantic and wonderful!" Mary signed. "What other places did you visit?"

"The Black Sea and Giza, where we saw the magnificent Sphinx. We enjoyed the people and their ancient cultural lifestyle in Giza. We felt as though we had been taken back in time to the reign of the Pharaohs. We enjoyed it very much."

When John fell silent, Mary enjoyed looking at the surrounding countryside. Once Ben tapped Mary on the shoulder and pointed to a wild turkey, awkwardly taking flight. Mary giggled as it reached the needed altitude and glided from view. Within minutes, three deer bolted across the road in front of them, spooking the team of horses.

John watched Mary's eyes light up with youthful excitement, and he silently recalled the day that he and Helene had reclaimed her from the orphanage many years ago.

I truly regret the years of separation, he thought. *But I am grateful for this time together.*

Suddenly he felt Mary's hand on his arm, and he turned to face her.

"Please tell me more, Papa."

"If you wish," he said. "One day, your mother and I attended a Water Festival with Sultan Abdul Hamid the Second. We were guests in the Riosk, the Sultan's private chamber. Helene's father, Theodore Baltazzi, held a high rank in the House of the Pasha, which influenced our immediate acceptance. Theodore Baltazzi was a tall and robust man with a mustache and typical Grecian features. He was a strict and authoritative disciplinarian with his children, but their financial welfare was foremost in his thoughts throughout his career. His greatest desire was to leave his children in a state of vast wealth."

"What did he do for the Pasha?" Mary inquired.

John hesitated before saying, "It was your grandfather's duty to locate, trade, and purchase beautiful women for the Sultan's harem. With his earned money, he invested in the toll bridge, connecting Galata with Istanbul. This venture literally bought him the bank within a short time.

"Emperor Franz Josef," he continued, "always insisted on meeting the fiance of each gentleman within the Austrian government prior to a marriage. Thus, upon our engagement, I took Helene from the Baltazzi Villa to Vienna. The Emperor was impressed! 'Gracing the halls with such beauty will bring me delight' the Emperor told me. Indeed, Mary, Helene had the grace, beauty, and charm of a Greek goddess"

"Please tell me about your wedding, Papa!" Mary signed excitedly.

"Typically Greek," he chuckled. "Three days of celebration with a continual flow of music, food, and wine. The groom was honored on the first day, the bride on the second, and our wedding ceremony took place on the third. The cathedral was filled with people from Hungary, Austria, Turkey, and Greece. The reception was held in the Great Hall of the Greek Embassy."

"It must have been beautiful," Mary signed.

"Yes, it was," John agreed. "For several years, we moved a great deal, but each time was a new and exciting adventure for both of us, Cairo to Constantinople to Alexandria, plus other exotic lands. After the birth of two children, Helene insisted that we find a permanent home for our family. That is when we settled in Vienna. She soon gained respect as an elegant hostess and entertainer.

"Meanwhile, I became a delegate of Austria and Hungary, Administrative Commission to the Egyptian State Department, and, in 1867, I became a Knight of the Austrian Leopold Order. Later, I was elevated to the Hereditary Knight Lord by the Emperor. In October, 1869, I received the Lesser Cross of the Royal Hungarian Order of St. Stephen. On January 30, 1870, I was granted the rank of Baron by the Emperor. Helene was quite pleased with her new title as Baroness Vetsera. And lastly, I became Ambassador to Russia and Cairo. The duties of this rank sent me away from home for extensive lengths of time."

As he fell silent, Mary closed her eyes, absorbing and envisioning the life and times of her prestigious father. Thus the miles rolled past in an ambience of quiet contemplation for the trio.

That evening, they stopped at an Inn to eat, sleep, and rest the horses. After eating steaks, bowls of pinto beans, and hot biscuits, the three travelers retired to John's quarters to visit before settling down for the night.

"That was one fine meal," Ben said. "I know that you are anxious to arrive home, Mary, but I am grateful we stopped for the night."

Mary smiled and nodded before signing, "Will you tell me more about our family, Papa?"

"What portion of our heritage are you interested in, Mary?"

Before she could respond, Ben said, "Perhaps you could tell her about the Baltazzi lineage of horses, John. I found that fascinating."

"Very well," John said. "As you know, Mary, your uncles have made quite a distinguished name for themselves among horse breeders throughout Europe. This venture began when Helene's father received a gift from the Sultan's private stables. The horse that he gave to him had won the 1876 Isle of Wight Derby in England. Indeed, some of the finest horses in the world are from Turkey. Aristide owned the Napajedi Stud Farm near Moravia, and Hector was an infamous gambler. Baltazzi son number three, Henry, was a Cavalry officer with the Fifth Hussars. He owned a stable and exercise course near Pardubice, Bohemia, near the estate of Countess Marie Larisch. A love and respect for quality horses attracted the Empress and the Countess to the Baltazzi family."

"I once heard that the Baltazzi brothers were highly ranked among the hunter sport," Ben said.

"Yes, that is true," John replied. "And they also introduced Polo to England. Although the game originated in India, the English horse enthusiasts rapidly accepted Polo as a favored equestrian sporting event."

Suddenly Mary signed, "Papa, my uncles were so good to me, and I already miss them very much. They once gave me a beautiful, white Arabian horse. The Viennese soon began to call me the niece of the four famous Turf Men, as I often rode my horse through Prater Park in the afternoons."

Mary audibly chuckled, which startled her father.

"What are you thinking about?"

"Uncle Alexander was always jovial and fun to be around," she signed. "Everyone enjoyed being with him. Uncle Hector was always so serious. He looked like an Army commander in his black coat and top hat. They were so different!"

John and Ben laughed as Mary paced across the floor, depicting first her happy Uncle Alexander and then her astute Uncle Hector.

"On that note, my daughter, you should go to bed," John laughed. "We have another long day ahead of us tomorrow."

Mary smiled and kissed her father on his cheek. At the door, she waved good night to Ben and quickly exited.

"Good night, Obscure Princess," John murmured. "Sleep well and have sweet dreams."

Moments later, Ben retired to his room. John pulled off his boots and laid down on the bed with his hands clasped behind his head.

I am so proud of my daughter, he thought. *It seems that she has regained her zest for life, regardless of the ill winds that she has faced. I must continue answering any and all questions that she may have on her ancestry.*

John slowly closed his eyes, allowing visions of Mary as a babe to enter his mind. Thus a tired but grateful Baron Vetsera slept as the moon slowly crossed the heavens and vanished below the western horizon. The young Baroness was returning home, and life once more felt comfortable and complete.

At dawn, the trio was again aboard the covered wagon and slowly traveling down the familiar road toward Muldoon. The air was fresh and sweet with the scent of budding flowers and foliage. Mary's eyes glistened with excitement and wonder as she watched colorful butterflies soaring near the wagon. When John pointed to a mother quail and her four babies beside the road, she smiled with the deepest of delight.

Mary's eyes lingered for a moment on the bird's offspring. *How much alike they appear*, she told herself, *but if one got to know them well, how much different each would probably prove to be in character.*

Suddenly, Mary turned to John and signed, "I am so different than Hanna."

"What do you mean, Mary?" he inquired.

"Countess Larisch and I were always going horseback riding or shopping or to lunch, but Hanna always stayed home. She was content to knit or work in the garden. I fear that I was a bit unkind to her at times. I did not understand her, Papa."

John smiled and patted her on the arm.

"You did nothing wrong. She was happy with her quiet, more sedate life, while you were an opportunist. If life became too wearisome, you simply spiced it up a bit. You should not feel that you abused your sister. She was quite content with her choice of entertainment."

"I loved Ladislaus and Franz very much," Mary signed. "I called them Ladi and Feri. My two brothers kept everyone busy! I was heartbroken when Ladislaus died."

John closed his eyes for a moment and nodded.

"I too remember that day. Shortly before boarding the ship for America, I read a newspaper item about the fire. There in my horror among the listed dead, I read my son's name."

"Yes, Papa," Mary signed. "Mama and Countess Larisch were preparing to attend the opera, and Ladi asked to accompany them. THE TALES OF HOFFMANN is very complex, Ladislaus,' Mama told him. Ladi said, 'Some of my friends have recommended it to me. Please, Mama. I truly wish to go with you.' Mama finally relented. During the third act, Ladi was absent, but Mama and Countess Marie were not concerned. They felt that he had joined his friends amidst the audience. Mid-way through Act Three, smoke began to billow forth from behind the stage. Soon, the velvet drapes were aflame, and smoke filled the building. With great difficulty amid the panic, Mama and Countess Marie slowly moved toward the main entrance. But, Ladi did not join them as they waited and watched the building become engulfed in flames. Countess Marie told me how Mama called out to her son, pacing between the firemen, asking if they saw him. Her dress was full of black soot as she pushed against the police and toward the flames still calling, 'Ladi, Ladi.' The tragedy encompassed all of Vienna, a nightmare that will never fade from the Austrian mind."

"That is true," John acknowledged.

"I am grateful for the wonderful times that we did share as a family" Mary motioned, "but, it seems impossible that life in Vienna is gone forever."

"Yes, now we must suffer for mistakes made by all of us," her father responded. "Even the Empress must forfeit her right to nobility if the deed tarnishes the throne, Mary. Marie, Ben, Frances, you, and I are examples of disobedience in the eyes of Austria. And, as Frances said, we must now begin life anew. Helene is quite content with her social standing in Vienna, and we must seek serenity in America."

"Yes," Ben said quietly. "And I, for one, am finding life in exile quite agreeable. The change has granted me a sense of new found freedom."

"Indeed," John replied. "We are finding serenity among the thorns wrought by the throne."

TWENTY-FOUR

SQUEALS OF EXCITEMENT GREETED THE TRIO IN THE COVERED wagon as the team trotted up the lane toward the home of the Vecera family. John tapped Mary on her shoulder and pointed to the little group who were waving from the veranda. Her gaze was already riveted on the scene, and she shivered with anticipation as the team came to a halt in front of the house. Tears of joy accompanied the embraces as Mary was reunited with her family. That evening, Annie served an exquisite dinner as a personal welcome for the Baroness. With Julia seated on her lap, Mary conveyed her fondness for her students and her appreciation for being with her family once again. As the family adjourned to the sitting room for coffee, Marie suddenly excused herself and ascended the stairs.

"Is something wrong?" Mary signed.

John glanced at the Empress.

"The Countess will return in a few moments," Frances assured them. "Actually, she has a surprise for you!"

Seconds later, Marie ran down the stairs and approached John with an envelope in her hand.

"This is addressed to all of us, but I am sure that you should have the honor of reading it first," she said quietly.

John accepted the correspondence and silently read the sender's name before gasping, "Helene! Mary, this is a letter from Helene."

Mary sat on the arm of her father's chair as he read the forbidden message from Austria.

My Dearest Family and Friends,

I pray that this arrives, for I am warned that contact with you may be dangerous. Cardinal Carl Kaspar advises me that he will forward my letter as official church business, and your parish priest will then see that you receive it. I indeed hope this is true.

We still live under the pretense of mourning for Mary. We assume that she is alive and well as we have heard nothing to the contrary. If this is true, my grandchild should be three-years-old now. Vienna has virtually forgotten Mayerling. Perhaps Johann Salvator, Rudolph's friend and cousin, could have prevented the assassination had he wanted to change Rudolph's mind about the hunting trip and forgetting the conspiracy against his father of overthrowing him from the Hungarian throne. But, alas, rumor tells of Johann missing, drowned and forgotten. How many falsified deaths will there be?

Between Mozart concerts and balls, the sound of the gun echoes across the racetrack, and the Viennese chant, "Let's go to the races!" My brother Hector has wed a minister's daughter, while Aristide has been appointed minister, Knight of the Austrian Leopold Order. My sisters continue to uphold our noble blue-blood. The Baltazzi Box at the racetrack continues to draw respect and admiration from those in attendance. But I comfort myself with the vision of our Turf Angel, gracing the event with her presence. My brothers have retained their gentlemanly charm, tipping their top hats and kissing the hands of the ladies of nobility.

Countess Larisch, the regal women of Vienna have not lost their zest for gossip. Rumor continues to provide the main entertainment for the elite.

> Emperor Franz Josef forbids Austria to speak of Mary Vetsera. Both local and foreign reporters are prohibited from mentioning the Vetsera name. I once wrote an item in hopes of restoring honor, but it was seized in the press room. The truth is repressed by the monarchy, and nothing can be done to release it. Perhaps this is the end of the dynasty. We are all very well, so do not worry for our sake.
>
> God bless you, John. I pray that you are with the others for your strength and wisdom are indeed essential.

The letter was signed, "Love, Baroness Helene Vetsera."

John stared at the letter for a moment without speaking. Then he rose to his feet and began to pace the floor.

"Eleven years," he exclaimed. "I have received no word from Helene in over eleven years. First, she lost me, then Ladislaus, and now Mary. She has to be a strong person to endure all that."

Frances stood up and walked toward John. She touched him on the arm as she quietly agreed, "Yes, John, Baroness Vetsera is indeed a strong individual. She and her family will survive and thrive under the Austrian regime, and we will survive and thrive in America. We have our Mary and little Julia to fill our lives with happiness and pleasure."

John smiled at the regal movement of her hand as she motioned toward the mother and daughter.

Marie also noticed the hint of nobility in the gesture.

"Yes," she laughed. "I believe we have sufficient reasons to stay busy!"

The Vecera family settled in a harmonious and happy lifestyle. Mary's lack of audible sensitivity was not considered a burden as the mother and her daughter re-established their bond. During the morning hours, the two shared love and laughter as they fed the chickens and visited the barn animals.

And, during Julia's afternoon nap, Mary slipped away to ride her horse and explore the Texas countryside. Each night, Julia brushed Mary's long hair in preparation for bedtime, but Annie was usually called upon to remove the locks from the brush.

Thus, it was not uncommon to see Mary, Julia, and even Frances playing hide and seek among the tall oak trees. The three of them often took long walks, sharing private thoughts with one another. Upon the trio's return, Annie and Marie graciously accepted wildflowers from Julia and Mary, placing the delicate foliage into vases of water.

Mary was now twenty-one-years-old, and her youthful and vibrant beauty shone forth as she glided through each new day. One afternoon, she tapped Marie on the shoulder as the Countess was brushing her hair.

"Where are you going?" she signed.

Countess Marie smiled and embraced the girl.

"I am going to town," she said. "Would you like for me to get you something new?"

"No!" Mary gestured. "I want to go with you."

Marie shook her head.

"I do not feel that your mother and father would agree. I am sorry."

Marie turned to leave, but again Mary tapped her on the shoulder.

"I want to go with you!" she signed.

Marie sighed and shrugged her shoulders.

"I would love to have you with me, Mary. I will wait while you ask Frances. All right?"

Mary smiled and nodded before running down the stairs to find the Empress. Marie followed at a more sedate pace. Hearing Frances speaking in a forceful voice, the Countess followed the sound to the study. Mary was standing in front of her mother frantically motioning with her hands.

"I miss being around others!" she signed.

"I am terribly sorry, Mary, but your father and I agree that it is still much too dangerous for you to be seen in town," Frances said.

Tears of frustration streamed down Mary's face as she signed, "I am a prisoner in my own home!"

"No, Mary," Frances responded. "You are not a prisoner in your own home. You must think of Julia's welfare as well as your own. No," she repeated, "you cannot go to town with Countess Larisch."

Marie stepped between the mother and daughter and faced Mary. She wiped the tears from her face with her handkerchief as she said, "Mary, you must obey the wishes of your parents. They do not want you hurt anymore. Understand?"

"But, I miss attending noble functions and the beautiful attire and the . . ."

Marie seized the deaf girl's hands for a moment. When she released them, she touched Mary on the cheek with one hand.

"Tomorrow morning, you and I will take a long horseback ride. Perhaps we can talk Annie into preparing a picnic lunch, and you and I can spend the entire day together."

"Yes," Mary signed with a faint smile on her lips. "That would be very nice. I just feel so isolated at times."

"We understand, Mary," the Countess replied. "Perhaps one day you will be able to join me on a trip to town, but now is not the time."

As Mary left the study, Frances shook her head.

"It is so sad," she murmured. "Mary is such a vibrant and beautiful girl, but we cannot risk the life of her or her child for an afternoon of shopping."

"I know," Marie said. "Tomorrow she and I will spend quality time together, and perhaps she will feel better."

"I will tell Annie to prepare a special lunch for you," the Empress responded.

"Thank you," the Countess replied. "I will not be in town long. I think Mary will be fine while I am gone. She just had a surge of homesickness for Vienna. Nothing more than we all experience at times."

Marie saw a fleeting smile appear on the lips of the Empress.

"Perhaps," she added with a wink, "not all of us experience this homesickness problem. It is possible that one Austrian prefers living in America!"

The Countess heard a soft chuckle as she turned and left the study.

At dawn the following morning, Marie and Mary left the house with the picnic in hand.

"Ben mentioned that he would have our horses saddled for us," Marie said. "But I failed to tell him that we would be leaving before the chickens awaken!"

Mary giggled and pointed toward the barn. Marie laughed after she followed the hand motion and saw John, standing beside two saddled horses.

"Good morning, John," she called. "You are up early this morning!"

"An early riser is required to stay one pace ahead of you two," he chuckled. "The weather seems favorable for your outing."

"Good morning, Papa," Mary signed. "It is going to be a beautiful day."

She kissed him on the cheek as he handed the reins of one horse to her. Marie handed him the little bundle of provisions, and he put them in the saddle bag of her mount. He waited and watched as they stepped into their stirrups and swung into the saddles.

"Have a wonderful day," he called as they trotted down the lane. "And be home by early evening."

Marie glanced over her shoulder and waved.

"Do not worry," she replied. "We will be safely home by late afternoon."

The morning hours passed quickly as Mary and Marie traversed the countryside and conversed by sign language. If one pointed, the other looked without question, and thus they enjoyed nature at its best. When the sun was directly overhead, Mary pointed to the saddle bag on Marie's horse and patted her stomach.

"I agree," Marie laughed. "Let's find a nice shade tree and have lunch."

Suddenly Mary reined her horse to a halt and pointed toward a draw south of them. A horse and rider were approaching in a lope. Marie quickly reined her horse between Mary and the stranger.

"Good morning," the man said as he trotted his horse up beside Marie and stopped. "It is a fine day for a ride."

"Indeed it is," Marie replied.

"My apologies," he said as he stepped from his horse. "My name is Vaclav Stancik."

"I am pleased to meet you Mr. Stancik," Marie replied. "I am Marie Vecera."

Vaclav tipped his hat. He then turned his attention to Mary.

He is tall, dark, and nice looking, Mary noticed as she smiled at him.

"I am on my way to the Vecera Estate right now," he commented. "John and I are discussing the trade and sale of Vecera horses. He is one of my best customers, plus a good friend."

Vaclav led his horse nearer to Mary, and again he tipped his hat. Although polite and gentlemanly, his gaze did not move from the face of the Baroness for several seconds.

"And what is your name?"

Basking within his attention and admiring gaze, Mary quickly signed, "M-a-r-y V-e-c-e-r-a. I am very pleased to meet you."

Vaclav watched her hand movements, and then, without speaking, he turned to Marie.

"This is John's daughter, Mary, Mr. Stancik," Marie explained. "She is deaf and does not speak. The movement of her hands is her way of communicating with you."

"I see," he said as he once again focused on Mary. "Please call me Vaclav. What did she say?"

"She told you that her name is Mary Vecera, and she is very pleased to meet you," Marie said.

"Indeed!" he replied. "I am very pleased to meet you also, Mary Vecera."

"Mary and I brought lunch with us, Vaclav. Would you care to join us? I am quite sure that Annie sent more food than Mary and I can possibly eat."

His gaze did not leave Mary's face as he said, "Yes, thank you. I would be honored to join you for lunch."

Mary's eyes sparkled with excitement as she read the reply on the lips of Vaclav.

She felt the warmth from his loving admiration course through her spirit. The setting was not of Viennese elegance, nor was the suitor of royal heritage. Rather, the destiny for this unsung Princess was set in the rustic American frontier, and the enamored admirer was of a rugged and robust lineage. Indeed, fate cast the Baroness from the arms of the Crown Prince and into the heart of a south Texas horse trader and sheep rancher.

TWENTY-FIVE

WITH THE PASSAGE OF TIME, VACLAV BECAME A REGULAR visitor at the Vecera Estate. Everyone enjoyed his sense of humor and friendly, easy-going nature. Mary was pleased as his business trips increased in time and frequency. Early one morning, Mary was on the south side of the house gathering fresh flowers when she saw Vaclav approaching with a second horse following on a lead rope. Annie was sweeping off the front veranda, and she waved and called as he approached the front entrance.

"Good morning, Vaclav."

"Good morning, Annie," he responded as he stepped off his horse and tied him to the hitching post. Then he led the chestnut quarter horse toward the front steps.

"That is a beautiful animal, Vaclav!" Annie gasped. "Did John purchase him?"

"No, Annie," he chuckled. "This one is not for sale. Is Mary up yet?"

Annie grinned and walked down the steps.

"Yes. I believe that she is in the garden. I will get her for you."

"That isn't necessary, Annie," he smiled. "There are some things that a man needs to do for himself!"

But Vaclav did not have to seek her out. At that moment, as if she had been mentally summoned, Mary slowly walked around the corner of the house and approached the horse trader. Her eyes glistened with admiration as she stroked the withers of the horse on the lead rope.

"Vaclav, he is beautiful!" she signed. "Did Papa buy him?"

"No, Mary," he responded. "I did. It's for you." He handed the lead rope to the deaf girl.

"For me?" she signed. "But why?"

Her hands darted in rapid movement, causing Vaclav to laugh out loud.

"Slow down, young lady, I can't read a word that you are saying."

"Thank you," she signed in slow motion. "I love him."

He smiled and touched her on the cheek.

"Good," he said. "He is the finest quarter horse in the country. You two will make a great team."

This gift sealed an unspoken bond between the young Baroness and the Texas horse trader. His business trips to the Vecera Estate now took two days rather than one as he and Mary rode their horses through the surrounding countryside. Their affection for one another was becoming more evident with each passing day.

One evening several months later, Vaclav joined John on the veranda. He sat down and leaned toward the Baron with his elbows resting on his knees. He cleared his throat to speak, hesitated, and leaned back in his chair.

A moment later, he again cleared his throat and leaned toward John. Then he shook his head and grinned.

"You know, John, I have bought, sold, traded, and bartered all of my life. And I have never been short of words," Vaclav mumbled, "until now!"

"You are not trying to sell me a horse, I take it," John laughed.

Vaclav stood up and paced back and forth in front of John.

"No sir, I'm not."

"What is it then?" John asked. "We have been friends for a long time now, and I have never seen you this nervous."

Vaclav stopped in front of John and put his hands behind his back.

"John," he suddenly blurted, "I would like to marry your daughter."

John remained silent for several seconds, and Vaclav resumed his pacing.

"Sit down, Vaclav," John demanded. "I cannot think with you running back and forth in front of me."

Vaclav sat down and tapped his fingers nervously on the arm of his chair.

"Have you spoken with Mary about this?"

The anxious man shook his head.

"I thought that I should talk to you first."

"Have you considered the difficulties that you may encounter due to her lack of hearing and speech?"

"Yes sir, I have," Vaclav nodded. "And I think it may be an asset at times. She is not apt to talk my ear off."

John burst into a fit of laughter. "You may be right, Vaclav," he said as he wiped the tears from his eyes. "If Mary agrees, you both have my blessing."

Mary was sitting with Julia on the porch swing on the north veranda when Vaclav walked around the house and paused in front of her. He gazed down upon her for a moment. His legs felt shaky as he thought about the question he was about to ask. He wanted to express his request more eloquently, but his nerves forced him to blurt out the simple, traditional words, "Will you marry me?"

Mary studied his face for a moment before signing, "I do not understand. What did you say?"

Vaclav put his hands on his hips and looked into her eyes.

"I said, Mary, will you marry me? Will you be my wife?"

"You are a good man, Vaclav," she slowly signed. "I was not expecting this. I do not know what to say."

"Your father has given us his blessing if you agree to marry me," he said and stepped back.

"I need some time alone to think," she motioned.

He nodded and tipped his hat to her.

"Of course, Mary," he said. "I should not have expected an instant reply. I will be in the house if you wish to talk to me."

After the hopeful horse trader disappeared from view, Mary looked down at Julia. The little girl grinned at her mother, and Mary motioned for her to follow. The two of them walked through the flower garden as Mary pondered about the difference in age, the altered life-style, and the transmutation from single to united.

But one thing I know, she thought. *My Julia needs a father!*

In the twilight of day, she paused and signed, "What do you think, Julia? Would you like a horse trader for a father?"

Julia giggled and covered her mouth with her hand. Mary smiled and nodded.

"Yes, my daughter," Mary signed. "I am going to say yes!"

Thus, preparations were set into motion for a wedding—a wedding that, it was decided, would take place after they had reached the church in Lovelady, the town nearest to where Vaclav lived. Although the vows would not be exchanged at the Vecera Estate with the family in attendance, everyone felt grateful to play a part in the planning. With Annie on the sewing machine and Marie helping with the design, the wedding dress was finally sewn and ready for the bride. Frances explained the ceremony to Julia and helped her choose the appropriate dress to wear.

The departure date finally arrived and the prospective groom rolled up in a buggy followed by a covered wagon which he had arranged to have driven to transport Mary's belongings. The men greeted Vaclav as he stepped down from the buggy and tied up his horse. He was wearing a dark suit and his boots were polished to perfection.

"Vaclav," John called from the steps of the veranda, "you look as though you are already dressed for the wedding!"

Vaclav grinned and tipped his new felt hat in acknowledgment.

"Well, John," he said with a chuckle, "I thought that I should try to impress my bride with a bit of Texas pride and dignity. Looks are deceiving though. I am nervous as a cat!"

John met Vaclav on the steps and put his hand on the groom's shoulder.

"You will make a fine husband and son-in-law," John reassured him. "Come in and sit down. Mary and Julia are about ready. We will have a cup of coffee and visit while we wait."

Meanwhile, the upstairs of the Vecera household was in utter chaos.

"Mary," Marie said, "let's put your hair up off your shoulders."

"It will not stay looking nice during our long journey," Mary signed. "Vaclav may not approve."

"You are the bride," Marie contended. "In Vienna, we often put it up, and you looked beautiful!"

"Let's do it. My husband should not complain if I look beautiful!" Mary signed with a giggle.

Annie suddenly burst into the room and, with a frenzied look in her eye, glanced about the cluttered chamber.

"I cannot find the blue garter that I made for Mary!" Her voice rose to near hysteria as she added, "Everything else is packed and ready to go, but I cannot find the garter anywhere!"

Mary and Marie glanced at one another and laughed. Marie pointed to Julia who was dancing in front of the full length mirror with the blue garter around her forehead. Annie snickered and patiently explained to the youngster that the band should be worn around the leg rather than the head.

"Your *mother's* leg," she added as Julia sat down and tried to put her foot through it.

Finally conceding defeat, Julia handed the garter to Annie.

"But, you can help me pack it in your mother's trunk," Annie added with a wink.

A moment later, the maid and child skipped out of the room en route to pack the undergarment. Mary and Marie were still giggling when Frances bustled in and announced, "Vaclav has arrived. He and John are having coffee in the sitting room. He looks like a true country gentleman, Mary. Perhaps you should exchange vows before arriving at your new home," she added with a wink.

Mary looked vibrant and poised with her hair fashioned in long curls down the back of her long sleeved white blouse with the stand-up collar. The long, dark-brown skirt rustled softly as she put her arms out and spun in a circle.

"Am I worthy of his last name?" she signed with a smile.

Frances caught her breath and gasped, "My child, you look wonderful!"

"We are almost finished with her hair, Frances," Marie said. "Please tell Vaclav that she will be down in a few moments."

Frances embraced Mary and kissed her on the cheek before quietly leaving the room.

As the door closed, Marie put her finger beneath Mary's chin and raised her head until the bride-to-be was looking straight into her friend's eyes.

"What is wrong?" Marie inquired. "You are trying to be the happy bride, but I know that something is bothering you. Are you sure this is what you want?"

A tear formed in the corner of Mary's eye and slipped down her cheek.

"I do not know if I honestly love Vaclav. Will love come later?" she signed.

"Perhaps, Mary," the Countess said. "Perhaps it will. I do not know. He is a good man, and he loves you very much. She smiled as she added, "Maybe your love will grow with time."

"I am not sure that I want to be a wife," Mary rapidly signed. "Nor am I sure that I want more children!"

"Give yourself time to adjust. And if you ever need any of us, Baroness Mary, we are here for you."

The unaccustomed usage of her title caused Mary to smile.

"Thank you, Countess," she responded with her hands and bowed.

Suddenly she grabbed Marie and embraced her. "I love you," she signed.

"And I love you, our beautiful Mary," Marie said. "We all love you very much."

Although neither spoke Rudolph's name, each lady felt his presence in the room. They both knew that this bond of love and understanding was strong and lifelong. This they shared before Mary and Vaclav departed from the Vecera Estate.

Moments later, Baroness Mary Vetsera and her dear friend Countess Marie Larisch descended the stairs together, walking straight and proud as they quietly joined the awaiting groom and family in the sitting room.

Sometime later, Mary, Vaclav, and Julia climbed into the buggy. As the sleek, well groomed horse trotted down the lane with the polished rig, Mary and Julia waved until trees and foliage hid them from view. A now fully-packed covered wagon followed the happy couple.

Once again, the Vecera family had watched as Mary departed from their lives. But this time, they were secure in the thought that she was a woman soon to be bonded to her husband and child under a vow of "til death do us part". This time, perhaps, the Baroness would find true happiness.

"May God be with you, my daughter," Frances said with a note of regret before turning and walking up the steps.

"Yes, my dear friend," Marie softly concurred. "May God bless and keep you."

As twilight descended upon the Texas countryside, the Vecera home was veiled in a forlorn silence. Julia's laughter did not echo through the house as was typical when she had played hide and seek before bedtime. Mary's smile was no longer present to lighten the hearts of those nearby as she kissed her mother and father good night.

Marie slowly ascended the stairs and entered her room. She put on her nightgown and brushed her hair before reclining on the bed. It seemed that many hours passed as she lay, listening to the lonely call of the night birds and the rhythmic chant of the crickets. "Perhaps Mary will write soon," she murmured sleepily, "and she will speak of the beauty in her world now." With this vision in her mind, the Countess drifted into peaceful slumber.

TWENTY-SIX

"THIS AREA IS CALLED THE PINEY WOODS OF TEXAS," VACLAV explained as they rode peacefully along. "But our ranch is located in the Lost Piney Woods."

"Why?" Mary signed.

"Because we are a long way from anywhere," he said with a chuckle. "And our home looks different than you are accustomed to, Mary. It is a one-room log cabin, but we have barns and corrals, and," he winked at Julia, "we have lots of animals."

Julia clapped her hands and giggled.

"Is our house pretty?" Mary inquired with her hands.

"I think so," Vaclav replied. "I call it Heaven."

The little family traveled for several days through a wonderland of tall trees, foliage, and wildflowers. Mary and Vaclav kept busy pointing to the various species of Texas wildlife and revealing the names to Julia. At one point in their journey, the little girl tapped Mary on the shoulder and pointed to an armadillo beside the trail.

"Turtle!" she exclaimed. "Broken turtle!"

Mary and Vaclav glanced at one another before bursting into laughter.

"You are probably right, Julia," Vaclav sputtered. "I do believe that you are going to add new meaning to Mother Nature."

Although the journey was pleasant and the scenery outstanding, after a number of days on the trail, the trio was growing weary and anxious to reach their destination. Julia was asleep on Mary's lap when Vaclav finally reined the horse to a stop.

"Welcome home!" he announced proudly.

Mary glanced up and saw a small cabin nestled among barns, corrals, and tall timber.

"That is our house?" she asked with rapid hand motions.

"Yes, Mary, we are home!"

He pointed to his chest and said, "I built it myself. It is small, but we have everything that we need. And, I cleaned it spotless just for you."

Julia sat up and looked around. She rubbed her eyes before jumping down from the buggy with an excited squeal. She waved her arms and immediately began to explore the territory.

Vaclav helped Mary down from the rig, then asked the man he had hired to drive the wagon to assist him with unloading Mary's belongings. As he paid and dismissed the driver and took the horse and buggy to the barn, Mary slowly walked up to the cabin and opened the door.

I thought Vaclav was teasing when he said that it was a one-room cabin!

Mary cautiously peered in at the crude fireplace and large stack of wood stored beside it. Her eyes widened in shock as she noticed the huge black cook stove sitting against the opposite wall.

In the first place, she mused, *I do not know how to cook, let alone trying to learn on that iron monster!*

A bed, a dresser, and a table with two chairs occupied the balance of the cabin's interior.

Mary gasped and covered her mouth with her hands. *What am I doing here,* she mentally chided herself. *What was I thinking?*

She felt Vaclav brush against her, and she turned to face him. His arms were loaded with bundles and baggage, which he set down in the middle of the room. He looked around the cabin before turning to Mary. She glanced down at the pile of personal belongings that were heaped in the middle of the small cabin, and then she looked at Vaclav. Suddenly she shrugged her shoulders and giggled.

Seconds later, Julia entered the cabin and abruptly stopped and stared at her mother and Vaclav. They were laughing and pointing at the displaced paraphernalia in the middle of the room. Mary noticed the worried expression on her child's face and attempted to regain control by wiping the tears from her eyes. But the cloud of disapproval in Julia's eyes rekindled the comical situation, and Mary again erupted in a fit of laughter.

That evening after supper, Mary and Vaclav sat on a bench outside of the cabin. The light of the moon cast shadows among the leaves on the trees, and moonbeams sparkled against the surface of the slow-moving stream. Julia was asleep, snugly tucked in a pallet on the floor, and the world seemed at peace. Mary sighed and leaned her head against Vaclav, and he gently turned her face toward him. In that precious moment, Mary felt that love and happiness could restore life after tragedy. As their lips touched, the Baroness silently conveyed, *perhaps this kind man will teach me to love once more, my dear friend Countess. Perhaps he will indeed.*

The family quickly settled into a comfortable, compatible life-style. Unable to quell Mary's fear of the iron monster, Vaclav took over the duties of cooking while the woman he loved struggled to adapt to her new environment. One morning after breakfast, Vaclav and Mary remained at the table with fresh cups of coffee.

"Vaclav," she signed sadly, "I am sorry that we have not had our wedding yet, for I have so been looking forward to it. I thought you were going to make arrangements long before now. When *are* we going to get married?"

"It is just that we are so far away from town, and it seems that time has flown much faster than I have realized since joining you and Julia. Besides, the priest will eventually make his rounds to this area to perform marriages, baptisms, and pray over the ill. It would be far better to wait for him. Traveling to the church in Lovelady is extremely rough and dangerous. There are no decent roads, only paths traveled by horseback."

"I understand," Mary signed with a smile.

"Thank you." Vaclav paused for a moment before adding, "And now, my pretty Mary, I have a surprise for you."

"How could you have a surprise for me?" she inquired with her hands. "You have not been anyplace to buy me anything."

A glint of humor emerged in Vaclav's eyes as he responded, "I have been trying to educate you in the ways of the west, Mary, but you do not yet understand. We can survive and live a good life without spending money in stores. Our livestock and garden supplies us with ample food, and our house is heated with wood from our trees."

He leaned back in his chair and smiled at the bewildered lady across from him. "I have been going into the woods each day, cutting timber for your new home."

Mary signed, "New house?"

Vaclav nodded, but before he could speak Mary was hugging him and signing, "Thank you, Vaclav! Thank you!"

"I will try to have it finished before Christmas," he said. "But I will need your help if we are to meet that deadline."

Her eyes glistened with renewed enthusiasm as she nodded and signed, "Just tell me what you want me to do!"

Thus, Mary and Julia joined Vaclav in the forest each day, assisting in the chopping, carrying, and placement of logs for their new home. The short breaks away from the project were spent cooking, cleaning, sewing, mending, and washing.

Mary was rapidly transforming into a self-sufficient woman with pioneer spirit.

As the days, weeks, and months sped by, the Baroness once again found herself to be with child.

"I am so tired, Vaclav. Do you mind if I rest today?" she asked one morning.

"You look exhausted, Mary," he replied. "Forgive me. I should have noticed. Don't do any work today. The baby may come at any time. I will be back this evening."

He kissed her on the cheek before hurriedly exiting the cabin. She lay down on the bed for several minutes, but her thoughts were with her family at the Vecera Estate.

I have not written them since we arrived, she thought. *Perhaps I will feel better if I start a letter to them instead of laying here thinking of them.*

Minutes later, she sat down beneath a tall live oak with a tablet and pen in hand and began writing.

Dearest Family,

It is virtually impossible for me to send a letter from our home in the Lost Piney as often as I would like. Vaclav does not get to a post office very often, but I hope that you will receive this within the next month or two. Julia loves our new life, especially the sheep, goats, chickens, and ducks. I told her that she takes after her grandmother in her love for animals. During the summer months, she and I spent a great deal of time in the woods, while Vaclav worked on our new house. The trees were green and cool throughout the hot months, and then, during the fall, the air was refreshing, and the trees were adorned in autumn coats of red, green, gold, and amber. Now we are in the rainy season, but today is warm and sunny. Our house is not yet completed, but we hope to . . .

A pain suddenly seared through Mary. She gasped and grabbed her stomach. *The baby! My baby is coming! Julia, where is Julia?*

When the contraction subsided, Mary quickly stood up and began looking for her daughter. After walking to the barn, she felt a second pain begin to build and quickly found a safe place to sit.

Minutes later, she opened her eyes and saw Julia running toward her. Her daughter was crying as she fell on her knees beside her.

"What is wrong, Mama," she screamed. "Did you fall?"

Mary held the little girl at arms length until she calmed down.

"No, Julia. I did not fall," she signed. "I am having the baby. Hurry, Julia. Go and bring back your father!"

In the twilight of dawn on the third day of February, daughter Mary was born in the log cabin of Baroness Mary Vetsera and Texas horse trader Vaclav Stancik. The proud father held the baby in his arms and formally introduced little Mary to her big sister. As the infant wriggled and sucked on her tiny fist, Julia giggled and kissed her on the cheek.

Vaclav leaned over the bed and looked in Mary's eyes.

"She is beautiful," he expounded with pride. "Just like her mother."

Mary smiled and closed her eyes. She basked within the loving warmth and love of her newborn's father. *Perhaps*, she thought, *Rudolph would have made the same comment upon the birth of his daughter. I will never know. And, in this special moment, the past is lost. My soul feels cleansed, and contentment placates my spirit.*

As the sun cast the first light of day upon the little cabin in Lost Piney, Mary and her newborn babe slumbered.

TWENTY-SEVEN

"VACLAV, OUR NEW HOME IS BEAUTIFUL!"

"Why, thank you, Ma'am," Vaclav responded with a doff of his hat. He embraced Mary and gently kissed her on the lips.

"I am truly pleased that you like it, Mary," he said. "I only regret that it took me so long to finish it."

"When can we transfer our furniture and belongings from the cabin?" she asked.

"I was thinking that we may start moving a few items the first part of next month," he teased.

She laughed and motioned for him to move out of her way.

The two story home was built with native timber. Vaclav's design and labor had produced a spacious abode that included a large living room with a fireplace, a kitchen with a walk-in pantry, and three bedrooms.

Julia watched the baby, while Vaclav and Mary transferred their household goods from the cabin to the new house. During the course of the move, Mary found the tablet that she had been using on the day of baby Mary's birth. She smiled as she read the letter that she had started. *The unfinished sentence should be explained*, she thought.

Vaclav was working in the barn, and both children were taking a nap when Mary located a pen and resumed the correspondence.

Several weeks have passed since I began this letter, but there is a reasonable explanation for the delay. Our new daughter, Mary, decided to make her debut as I was writing you. She is beautiful and extremely healthy, and Julia adores her. Vaclav is a wonderful father to both children. He is a kind and generous man who continues to shower me with love and praise. We are now living in a new home that he built for us. Each morning, my daughters and I walk through the beautiful garden, and each time my mind returns to each one of you. Frances, are you still enjoying the magnificent flowers in your garden? Marie, who accompanies you on your horseback rides since I left? Papa, oh how I miss you! Who is buying and selling your fine horses for you, since I stole your horse trader? Annie, you will not believe this, but I enjoy cooking now. Vaclav even compliments me on my loaves of bread and occasional pastry. Although I miss you all very much, life is indeed sweet and serene. Since you are unable to share personal contact with my children, perhaps you will send a list of names for future use. Vaclav and I are hoping for more, and your suggestions for names will add special meaning to our family.

My love to you always, Mary.

She carefully addressed an envelope and slipped the letter inside. She held the letter to her bosom as she gazed through the bedroom window at the colorful myriad of wildflowers in the meadow below. Homesickness for her beloved family suddenly engulfed her, and tears streamed down her cheeks. Feeling a tug on her skirt, she turned and saw Julia. The child was looking up at her with a worried frown on her face.

Her little chin trembled with emotion as she asked, "Mama, what is wrong? Are you okay?"

Mary smiled and nodded. She quickly retrieved a handkerchief from the bureau drawer and dried the tears from her face. Then she motioned for Julia to sit down on the bed beside her.

"Julia," she signed, "do you remember your grandfather and grandmother?"

Julia smiled and nodded. "They were nice to me."

Mary smiled in agreement and signed, "Do you remember Marie and Annie?"

"Yes," Julia replied. "Marie was nice, and Annie was fun. She played hide and seek with me."

"Yes she did," Mary signed with a chuckle. "Usually at your bedtime!"

"You must always remember them, Julia," Mary signed with definitive hand motion. "They love us very much, and we must never forsake them."

The mother hugged the child before rising to her feet.

"And now, little lady," Mary signed, "we must prepare your father's dinner. He will be arriving soon, starved to death!"

With the letter clutched in her hand, Mary left the room with Julia following closely behind.

Vaclav did make a trip to town shortly thereafter, and thus, within weeks, the Vecera family received their first correspondence from the Baroness since her departure months ago.

As darkness descended, the wind swayed the limbs of the trees, and rain pattered gently against the windows of the Stancik home. With the arrival of winter, the daylight hours were minimal. Evenings were now long and enjoyable as the family shared happy times together. The living room felt warm and cozy as Vaclav walked over to the fireplace and added a log. The wood popped and cracked as flames ignited and sent sparks upward.

Mary looked at six-year-old Julia who was playing on the floor with little Mary. *It does not seem possible that little Mary is two-years-old now*, Mary thought. *Nor does it seem possible that I am sitting here with our daughter Caroline in my arms.*

Vaclav touched her on the cheek and smiled.

"You look beautiful, Mary, but you seem to be in deep thought," he said. "Are you feeling all right?"

"Yes," Mary signed. "I was just thinking about how fast time seems to be passing. We now have three children, and yet we are still not married, Vaclav. I am truly happy, but marriage is very important to me."

Vaclav assured her that they would be married soon and the matter was dropped.

Three months later, the priest rapped on the front door of the Stancik ranch house. Julia opened the door before running to find her mother.

Shortly, Mary was smiling at the priest and motioning for him to enter. He looked tired and dusty from his journey through the untamed portion of Texas, and he gratefully accepted the offer.

As though on cue, Mary whirled around and ran up the stairs. Her hands trembled as she pulled the wedding gown from the trunk. Julia watched from across the room as the bride frantically tried to fasten the fitted garment over her noticeably heavier frame.

"Julia honey, please help me," she finally signed.

With the mother and child both holding and fastening buttons, the bride soon stepped in front of the mirror and brushed her hair.

This is not exactly the wedding that I portrayed in my mind, she thought. *But, at this point, I am just grateful to exchange vows before a priest!*

Seconds later, Mary motioned for Julia to locate Vaclav and bring him inside at once. Wide-eyed and grinning, the child sprinted through the yard and disappeared from sight.

Moments later, she returned with Vaclav in tow. He was laughing and talking to the child as they ran up the steps and into the house.

"The priest has arrived, Vaclav," Mary signed as he came to an abrupt halt beside her. "Now we can get married!"

Vaclav stared at the woman in the wedding gown. His mouth was wide open, but he seemed unable to speak for a moment. Mary did not notice.

Mary, attired in white, and Vaclav, dressed in soiled work clothes, stood before the priest in the living room of their home, exchanging wedding vows. As baby Carrie began to cry, Vaclav motioned to Mary, and Mary quickly signed for Julia to hold the infant. So it came to pass that Julia held the babe in one arm and the hand of little Mary with the other. And thus, Vaclav Stancik and Mary Vecera were indeed united in Holy matrimony with God and their three bewildered children bearing witness to the union.

As the priest left the house, Mary embraced her husband. With cheeks aglow and eyes shining with happiness, she kissed him.

"Don't, Mary!" Vaclav said gruffly, pulling away. "Not now."

"Why not?" she signed "What is wrong?"

He hesitated for a long moment before answering. "Nothing. It is just that I am not very presentable right now. Besides, I have a lot of work to do."

Her eyes searched his face, hoping to catch a glimpse of the humorous expression that always made him so endearing to her. But at the moment it was absent.

As Vaclav headed back out the door, a frustrated Mary stood motionless. She had so hoped that her husband would have displayed more enthusiasm for their wedding. Perhaps he just needed more time to adjust to the fact that they were now actually joined in matrimony.

TWENTY-EIGHT

For several years, Vaclav and Mary Stancik enjoyed life together, sharing happiness and stability within their family unit. Mary occasionally received letters from the Vecera Estate, which helped fill the void of their presence in her life. At one point, Countess Larisch mentioned that Empress Elizabeth was going to return to Austria for a time. This possibility concerned Mary, but her response was filled with love and hope for her safe journey.

The Stancik family increased in number with the birth of Joseph, whom they called Joe, and two years later, they were blessed with a second son, Franz, nicknamed Frank. And, four years after Frank, baby Millie arrived in their lives.

Since the ranch was located in a scarcely populated area, schools were not available for the children. Thus, Mary taught them at home. Although Vaclav often traveled to LaGrange or Lovelady for supplies, Mary and the children never accompanied him.

One evening, Joe and Frank suddenly saw Vaclav's familiar team and wagon approaching the house. Their father had been away from home for over one week, and the sight of him sent the youngsters into an outburst of excited shrieks.

"Pa is home!" six-year-old Joe yelled. "Go tell Mama, Frank. Pa is coming up the road!"

As the four-year-old younger brother raced into the house, Joe ran out to meet his father.

"Hello, Son," Vaclav said as the boy jumped on the side of the slow-moving rig. "I brought you and Frank a present."

"What did you bring us, Pa?" the boy asked excitedly.

Vaclav chuckled and nodded toward the back of the wagon. "Crawl back there and look."

Joe scrambled over the side and saw a black and brown dog, nestled between the supplies in a corner of the wagon bed. The animal raised his head and whined.

"He looks great, Pa," Joe declared. "Where did you get him?"

"It is a long story, Son. I will tell you about him later. Right now, he needs some food. Can you and Frank find him something to eat?"

"Sure Pa," Joe replied. "Hey, Frank! Look what Pa brought us."

With the supplies unloaded and the team unharnessed and fed, Vaclav and Mary sat down at the kitchen table with freshly brewed coffee in front of them.

"Now," Mary signed, "tell me about the dog. I get the feeling that you have a story to tell about him."

Vaclav laughed and said, "You are right, Mary. He did join our family under strange circumstances."

Julia entered the kitchen, and Vaclav smiled and said, "Julia, why don't you get your brothers and sisters, and I will tell you all about my return trip home."

With Joe and Frank on the floor beside the dog and the rest of the family grouped around the table, Vaclav leaned back in his chair and smiled.

"Night before last, I camped beside a stream and ate a cold bite before getting out my bedroll. After traveling hard all day, I was very tired and slept especially sound. When I awoke yesterday morning, I noticed that somebody had been in my wagon. I took a fast inventory of our supplies and found that the sack of flour was missing."

"Somebody stole our flour?" Mary signed.

"That's right," Vaclav said. "They did not take anything else, which surprised me. There was coffee and sugar and beans right beside it, but only the flour was gone."

After the murmurs from the children died down, Vaclav continued.

"I was just grateful that they had not stolen the team and wagon."

"They could have killed you, Vaclav, while you were sleeping!" Mary's hands darted in rapid motion.

"Well, they didn't," Vaclav chuckled. "Anyway, I hitched up the team and started toward home. After traveling about three miles, I noticed an old covered wagon that had been pulled into a thicket. An old, skinny horse and a cow was tied to one side of it. A man and woman were cooking something over an open fire, while four youngsters and a starved dog watched from a distance. When I walked up to the camp, the couple smiled and shook hands with me. One of the little boys said 'Want to eat with us, Mister?' Before I could answer him, the man and woman repeated the invitation, adding that they did not have much. But they would be honored to have me join them. I looked behind their wagon and saw my sack of flour sitting on the ground against the wheel."

"What did you do, Pa?" Joe asked. "Did you tell them that you wanted your flour back?"

"No, Son, I didn't," Vaclav replied. "I looked at those hungry youngsters, the starved livestock, and the desperate mother and father and said that I would be honored to join them."

"Good," Mary signed. "I am glad that you did not mention the stolen flour."

"How did you get the dog, Pa?" Frank asked. "What about the dog?"

"Well, Son, I am coming to that. After we had eaten a meal of gravy over stale bread, I thanked them and said that I needed to head toward home. The whole family walked me to my rig, and just as I started to step up into the wagon, I glanced into the back of it. 'Doggone it,' I said. 'I forgot to buy flour! My wife is going to need some. Would you sell me some of yours?' I asked."

The Stancik family laughed, which caused baby Millie to clap her hands and giggle.

"I bought some flour from them, and, as I turned to go, one of the little boys tugged on my sleeve. 'Mister,' he said, 'would you please take my dog? He gets very hungry, and I know that you will take good care of him.' I looked at the man and woman, and they both nodded. 'We would be grateful' the man said. 'We barely have enough food for ourselves.' The little boy had tears streaming down his face, but he put the dog's lead rope in my hand. 'Please, Mister,' he said. 'His name is Turban, and he is a good dog.' I accepted the rope and ruffled the boys hair with my hand. I promised him that my two boys would take very good care of Turban."

Vaclav looked down at Joe and Frank. Turban was resting his chin on Joe's knee, while Frank gently caressed the top of his head.

"We will, Pa," they both promised.

Vaclav looked at Mary and winked.

"I am sure you will, Boys," he said quietly.

And thus, Mary, Vaclav, and their six children welcomed the gaunt creature into their family. Indeed, Turban seemed to sense the new found goodness in his life. He licked the hand of each Stancik lad before yawning and curling up in a cozy corner.

Later that night, Mary opened a letter from Muldoon that Vaclav had brought from town. Her hands trembled as she began to read the familiar scribe of Countess Marie Larisch.

Dearest Mary,

Empress Elizabeth did indeed sail back to Europe. Her appearance in Austria was met by disfavor from Franz Josef, and she is now safely back home.

Mary set the letter on the desk for a moment. *Thank God,* she thought with relief. *It would have been very simple for the Emperor to dispose of her.*

The balance of the letter was soothing to the Baroness. Everyone seemed fine and very happy to have Frances with them again. Mary smiled as she folded the correspondence and slipped it in the envelope.

"You are smiling. You must have received good news," Vaclav said as he entered their bedroom and shut the door.

"Yes," Mary signed. "They are all doing very well."

Vaclav sat down on the bed and rested his elbows on his knees. Suddenly he covered his face with his hands and shook his head. Mary immediately sat down beside him.

"What is wrong?" she signed.

Vaclav looked at her a moment before replying, "I have not wanted to worry you, Mary, but the territory is becoming increasingly dangerous."

"What do you mean?"

"Lovelady for instance," he said. "The town is filling up with immigrants and displaced outlaws. Now it is filled with Arkansas hillbillies, Louisiana cajuns, and Texas cattle ranchers and farmers. The only law is voluntary, and a hanging takes place about every day now. The Town Saloon is owned by a wealthy and powerful man who encourages troublemakers."

"We are safe here, though, aren't we?" Mary signed.

"We are okay for now," he responded. "But we must always be alert. Lawlessness in Lovelady could mean trouble for us. Many of the hardened outlaws are stowaways from foreign ships. Their desperate struggle to survive may be deadly for us. Do you understand, Mary? We must not only fight for our home, but we must be certain that we win!"

She nodded and tried to reassure him. Although he did not speak of it again, Mary often saw him pacing the floor during the night. Meanwhile, the Stancik children slept peacefully in an ambience of security, confident their mother and father were a fortress against adversity. And thus, time passed.

TWENTY-NINE

MARY WAS GATHERING FRESH VEGETABLES FROM THE GARDEN one afternoon when Carrie suddenly appeared at her side.

"Come quick, Mama!" she said as she tugged on her long skirt.

"What is it, Carrie?" she signed. "What is wrong?"

"Come and see what Turban is doing," the child insisted.

Mary set the basket of vegetables down and followed the youngster. After winding down the trail toward the stream, Carrie suddenly stopped and pointed at the two boys and dog standing near the water's edge. As the mother approached, neither boy noticed. Turban was barking and running around a rattlesnake that was coiled near Joe. With each strike, the dog outmaneuvered the viper, drawing attention away from the terrified youngster. Mary gasped and slowly reached for Joe. When she had a firm grip on his arm, she immediately jerked him up and away from the snake. She quickly located a long limb that had fallen from a tree and thrashed the rattlesnake until the limb finally broke, and she fell to her knees, exhausted and emotionally spent. Turban continued to growl and bite the venomous viper, even long after it was dead.

"You must be more careful!" Mary chastised her older son with hand motions.

"Turban saw him first, Mama," Joe cried. "Frank and I were just going down to the water when I saw that snake sitting up and looking my way. Honest, Mama, he didn't even rattle until Turban was almost on top of him."

"Then," Frank excitedly added, "that old snake stopped looking at Joe and started trying to bite Turban."

Mary pushed the hair away from her eyes and signed, "It is dead now. Let's go to the house."

That night at supper, little hands were sneaking every other bite of food to the canine hero. Mary blushed when Vaclav caught her sliding a piece of her fried chicken from her plate and offering it to the conqueror beneath the table.

Several days later, Mary was baking bread when she again felt a frantic tug on her skirt. Frank was motioning for her to follow him.

"Hurry, Mama," he said. "We can't get him off her!"

Mary's heart was pounding as she followed the little boy through the yard in a run. Joe, little Mary, and Carrie were standing at the base of a big oak tree. Carrie was crying and holding something in her hand.

"What is happening?" Mary frantically signed as she approached the little group.

"It's Carrie," Joe exclaimed. "We found some baby squirrels in that tree, and Carrie wanted to take one home."

"It bit her, Mama," little Mary declared, "and it won't let go!"

Mary looked down at Carrie's hand. The child's index finger was indeed securely affixed between the teeth of a small squirrel. The expression on the little girl's face was a combination of fear and anguish as she tried to pry her finger out of the little critter's mouth. Mary grabbed the squirrel and shook it vigorously. Although Carrie was released from the forest creature, her finger had been severely gashed. The concerned mother grabbed the child up in her arms and ran to the house. Bandages soon stopped the blood flow, but infection in the wound was just cause for concern for several days to follow.

"Here, Mary," Vaclav finally said. "Use this on Carrie's finger. It may kill the infection."

Mary glanced down at the perspiring child before signing, "What is it?"

"Turpentine. I don't know if it will help or not, but it may," he said.

Mary nodded and quickly began to unwrap the injured hand. She doused the hand and a fresh bandage in the strong scented liquid. Carrie groaned and writhed on the bed as the provisional medication stung the wound. Mary dampened a cloth and placed it on the child's forehead.

Throughout the night, Mary and Vaclav stayed in the room beside Carrie's bed. They placed cool compresses on her forehead and prayed as the hours passed.

Then, as the sun peered over the eastern horizon, Mary suddenly shook the dozing Vaclav.

"It worked!" she rapidly signed.

Vaclav stood up and looked at the child. Her eyes were open, and she smiled as he approached the bed.

"Hello, Pa," she said softly.

"How is my girl?" he smiled.

"I feel better, Pa," she quietly replied. "My hand doesn't hurt so bad, but I am very tired."

"Sleep now, Carrie," he whispered. "Your mama and I will be here if you should need us."

Mary rested her head on Vaclav's shoulder as they walked out of the room. As they entered the living room, he stopped and put his palm beneath her chin.

"Mary, you are exhausted. You rest now. Julia and I will take care of the chores and the younger children."

Mary smiled and nodded before signing, "First, I am going to thank God for sparing our Carrie."

Vaclav kissed her gently on the lips and whispered, "I love you, Mary Stancik."

One evening after the younger children were in bed, Vaclav asked Mary and Julia to join him at the kitchen table.

"I have not wanted to worry you," he said grimly, "but now I must talk to you for your own protection."

Mary felt her heart pounding with fear of the unknown. *Vaclav is truly scared for us*, she silently fretted. *I have never seen him so upset!*

"Julia," Vaclav continued, "I am depending on you to be by your mother's side at all times, when I have to be away from home."

"What is it, Pa?" Julia asked. "We have always gotten along real well during your business trips."

"I know you have," he said quietly, "but a new threat recently entered our territory, and I must train you and your mother to defend yourselves and the younger children."

"What are you trying to tell us, Vaclav?" Mary asked in an agitated manner. "What are we going to be fighting?"

"Indians," he replied. "Renegade Indians."

Mary glanced at Julia and shook her head. Since arriving in America, she had been told tales of the vicious deeds committed on settlers by marauding tribes. Now the stories felt real and a potential life-threatening danger to the Stancik family. Suddenly a tremor of fear coursed through her.

"We must leave at once!" Mary signed. "They will bring pillage, rape, and murder to us and our land."

"Stop!" Vaclav ordered. "I have been hearing of this problem for several months. The renegades are still some distance away from here, but they do seem to be coming this direction. I am going to teach you and Julia about guns. We have time for you both to learn how to handle firearms, and I want you both to be able to hit your target. We will start practice in the morning."

Vaclav stood up and left the table without a backward glance.

Mary groaned and rested her forehead on the table. Tears streamed down her face. Suddenly she felt Julia beside her, and she looked up.

"It will be okay, Mama," the girl said. "Don't worry. I will be with you always."

Mary reached out and pulled her oldest child toward her. *Oh, my sweet Julia*, she thought. *How can I explain my fear of guns to you? How could I possibly make you understand the pain of seeing your father, crumpled upon the snow in a pool of his own blood, murdered by a man with a pistol? But*, she quickly convinced herself, *that is part of the past. We must plan for tomorrow.*

Mary stood up and gently brushed the hair back from Julia's eyes.

"I love you very much," she signed. "You are right. We will be fine. Tomorrow you and I will begin lessons with your father."

The mother and daughter embraced before retiring to their rooms for the night. Vaclav was asleep when Mary entered the room and shut the door behind her. She walked to her bureau and pulled out a writing tablet and pen before glancing at Vaclav once again. He was still resting quietly, so she sat down on a bench by the window. She gazed at the stars twinkling in the heavens for a moment before shaking her head and gliding the pen across the paper.

My Dearest Vecera Family,

I hope this finds you all well. For the first time in many years, a situation has arisen that recalls Mayerling with vivid clarity. Vaclav intends to teach Julia and me the art of shooting firearms. I write of this only because I know you will understand my feelings on the matter. Vaclav insists that we become proficient at defending ourselves

> against a possible attack by renegade Indians. My mind knows that he is right, but my heart fights the very thought of holding a gun.

Mary stopped writing and put the tablet on the floor next to her. *I have said it*, she thought, *and now I feel better.*

She glanced up at the stars once again before picking up the tablet and pen. After quietly replacing them inside the drawer, she crawled into bed beside Vaclav.

It is late, and I must rise early in the morning. As Countess Larisch once told me, I am about to embark on another adventure. The Baroness smiled bravely before stretching out on the cool sheets and closing her eyes. *Yes, indeed. A new adventure.*

Within two weeks, Julia became an expert marksman. Mary was proud of her daughter's accomplishment, but she was unable to match the seemingly natural talent of the young girl.

Vaclav seemed to relax a bit. One afternoon he took his wife and daughter away from the house to test their skills on moving objects. As they stepped onto the bank of the river, he pointed to a piece of driftwood floating mid-stream.

"Hit it, Julia," he commanded.

Without hesitation, Julia brought her rifle up, aimed, and fired. The target bounced across the water and landed on the opposite bank.

"Good," her father said.

He pointed to a large oak leaf drifting on the water's surface.

"Now you, Mary," he said. "Hit it."

Mary raised the gun to her shoulder, shivered, and closed her eyes before firing. The dry leaf continued downstream, undisturbed by the bullet that had entered the water several feet behind it.

"Well," Vaclav grinned, "maybe those renegades are watching. If so, they have probably learned that between you and Julia, they are in trouble coming or going."

He slipped his arms over the shoulders of his two students and they walked back toward the house. As they entered the clearing south of the barn, he suddenly stopped.

"Shhh," he warned the mother and daughter. "Get down."

They fell to their knees in the tall grass and peered toward the corrals. Two bronze-skinned men in loin cloths were leaving the chicken house. They both had two chickens in each hand, carrying them by the legs. Julia started to stand up and fire at them, but Vaclav pulled her back down beside him. He held the gun with one hand and firmly shook his head. Mary held her breath as the Indians suddenly stopped and looked in their direction, but, seconds later, they vanished into the woods.

"Why did you stop me, Pa?" Julia asked. "I could have hit at least one of them from here."

"You may kill one, Julia," he said grimly, "but the death of one may bring dozens more. No. You do not shoot unless they are personally threatening you with bodily harm."

His attitude was icy cold as he added, "Do you understand? Do not shoot unless you absolutely have to!"

"Yes, Pa," Julia replied quietly. "I understand."

Vaclav looked at Mary.

"This is just the beginning. There will be many more."

The trio rose to their feet and hurried toward the house.

"Thank God," Mary signed as they entered.

The five children were playing school at the table in the kitchen. They looked up and grinned as their father, mother, and older sister entered the room.

"The children are all right!" Mary rapidly signed. "They do not even know that the Indians were here."

Vaclav nodded grimly and said, "Let's hope we keep it that way."

And thus, the Stancik family found themselves under siege. Without firing a shot or aiming an arrow, the renegades slowly and methodically drained the livestock, supplies, vegetables, and self-confidence from the man, woman, and their six children. Joe and Frank no longer enjoyed cool afternoon swims in the river. Little Mary, Carrie, and Millie no longer looked forward to gathering the eggs or picking wildflowers in the meadow. Vaclav increased his days away from home, and Julia became Mary's shadow against adversity. Indeed, the siege soon confirmed that a house divided cannot stand. As dusk settled upon the barren and lonely ranch home, Mary wept for yesterday.

THIRTY

FROM THE KITCHEN WINDOW ONE AFTERNOON, MARY AND ALL of the children watched as four Indians roamed around the ranch, looking for food. They entered the chicken house and soon returned with a handful of eggs.

"What are those old Indians going to do with our eggs?" Joe asked with a grin. "Have an egg fight?"

Frank and the girls giggled, but Mary motioned for them to be quiet.

The Indians turned their attention to the storage shed. After a few minutes inside, they came out with a barrel of peanuts. After setting the container in an upright position, they pulled the lid off. With both hands filled with the foreign, fully-shelled edibles, they popped them into their mouths and started chewing.

Seconds later, all four men sputtered and spit, glaring at the full barrel of goober peas.

Mary and Julia looked at one another and laughed.

"If we have nothing else to eat," the mother signed, "we will have peanuts!"

"Look," Frank said, "They are going to the chicken house again."

"The renegades are still looking for food," Julia whispered. "And they just might decide to take you home with them for supper." She paused and looked at Frank before adding, "And I don't mean so that you can eat with them!"

Everyone sighed with relief as the renegades ran across the meadow and disappeared into the woods.

Mary sat down and covered her face with her trembling palms. Julia walked over and put her hand on her mother's shoulder.

"They are gone now, Mama," she said. "Perhaps they will not return."

Mary looked at her daughter and slowly shook her head.

"I am afraid," she signed. "The Indians keep coming back, and your father seldom returns home anymore." She paused before adding, "And, when he does come back from town, the supplies are outnumbered by the whiskey bottles."

"I am with you, Mama," Julia reminded her. "I will help you, and we are going to be fine."

More than two weeks passed, but still Vaclav had not returned from his latest trip to town. The morning air felt warm to Mary as she went to the barn and storage shed to inventory the balance of their supplies.

Suddenly Julia ran toward her with the rifle in her hand. She pointed toward the lane that led to their house.

"Horses and riders, Mama," she yelled. "Come in the house. Hurry!"

Mary lifted her long skirt and ran as fast as she could. The mother and daughter quickly entered the house and shut the door behind them.

Seconds later, one rider dismounted and walked up the steps to the front door.

"Pa!" Joe yelled. "It's Pa. He has come home."

Julia stood beside Mary as the five younger children ran to greet him. He hugged each one before walking over to Mary.

"Sorry," he said.

The heavy scent of whiskey prompted Mary to step away from him.

"Look, I said that I was sorry. Didn't you understand me?"

With her eyes full of anger, she nodded and signed, "Yes, I understood. But where are the supplies that you went after, Vaclav? The children are hungry. Eggs, peanuts, and goats milk will not do it."

"Well," he grumbled, "I ran into a little trouble in town. While I was asleep in my room at the hotel, somebody stole all of my money."

Mary felt nausea rise within her, but she did not respond. As though everything was explained and settled, Vaclav walked into the house. He put his hands on his hips and glanced around the room.

"The place looks good," he said. "I brought a farmhand from town to help with the chores. I told him that he could bunk in the barn."

He turned to Joe and said, "His name is Henry, Son. Go help him get settled."

As the man of the house excused himself and went upstairs to their bedroom, Mary saw the sick look in Julia's eyes. She embraced the young girl for a prolonged moment.

There is nothing I can say to this child, she thought. *Julia truly shares in my heavy burden.*

The sun was mid-way to the western horizon when Vaclav awoke and came downstairs. His eyes were red, and the usual clean-shaven face was covered with whiskers.

"Where is your Ma?" he asked in a gruff voice.

Carrie pointed toward the door, and he nodded.

"Are you all right, Pa?" she asked quietly. "You don't act like yourself."

"Sure," he grumbled as he walked to the door and opened it. "I'm just fine."

Mary and Julia were in the garden, attempting to salvage some of the precious produce, when Vaclav appeared.

"Mary, I need to talk to you," he said. "Will you come inside for a minute?"

"Julia and I are about through," she cautiously signed. "Why don't you clean up and shave. I will be in soon."

He nodded and retraced his steps to the house.

Julia waited until he was out of sight before asking, "Mama, what is wrong with Pa? He looks and acts so different!"

Mary touched her on the cheek and then signed, "I know, Julia. I believe the whiskey has taken control of his thinking. He does not seem to care about us or himself anymore. I just don't know what to do about it."

Julia shrugged and said, "Maybe he will quit drinking, and then we can be a family again."

"Perhaps," Mary signed with a smile. "Perhaps he will at that."

One hour later, Mary and Vaclav sat down on their bed to talk. Mary felt hope building within her as she gazed at Vaclav. His face was clean-shaven, and his fresh clothes held the faint scent of soap. His hair was neatly combed, and his boots were polished and shined.

"Mary," he said, "LaGrange is a good place to conduct business. I am going back there with a few more of our horses. I can sell them and get the supplies we need."

Mary's nerves grew taut as doubt swept through her. A moment later, she stifled the negative instinct and smiled.

"When do you plan to leave?"

"Right now," he replied. "The earlier start that I get, the faster I can return with the supplies. Henry will be here to help you."

"This is why you needed to speak with me?"

He looked down at the floor and nodded. After a brief hesitation, the horse trader raised his head and looked at her.

"My luck has been running a little bad. I was afraid you might not agree with my leaving again so soon."

"I understand," she signed, "but do hurry home."

Thus, Mary, her six children, and Henry bid Vaclav a fond farewell as he left the ranch, leading all but the last of the Stancik horses.

Mary smiled and waved as Vaclav suddenly stopped and looked over his shoulder.

"I'll be back in a week or so with supplies," he called before kicking his horse into a lope and vanishing into the growth of green trees.

Mary felt calm and secure that evening as she tucked her youngsters into bed and retired to her room. She removed her nightgown from the bureau drawer and turned to disrobe. Suddenly she noticed that the lid of her personal trunk was unlatched, and the hem of her wedding dress was protruding from beneath it.

The girls must have been playing dress-up again, she smiled. *I so do wish they would be careful to put things back as they found them.*

She lifted the gown from the compartment, expecting to repack the garment before securing the latch. But her eyes widened in horror as she saw the lower content in total disarray. The cash box had been opened, and the majority of her currency was missing.

Vaclav!

She fell to her knees beside the modest remains of her Austrian heritage and wept. The Baroness had thrived within the brief moment of happiness with the Texas horse trader, and the thought of his treachery now sickened her. The time with him had been warm and wonderful. Their life together began with his kindness and love for Julia, culminating with five captivating Stancik children. His betrayal of love and concern now left the deaf woman in a state of anguish and distress.

Hours passed with Mary curled beside the violated trunk. Visions from the past blemished plans for the future as she attempted to sort through recent events.

Six children await my love and guidance! she finally reminded herself. *In spite of the void in our lives and hearts, I must create a new life for my family.*

As dawn cast a golden glow upon the horizon, Mary slowly rose to her feet and staggered to the window. Through red and swollen eyes, she looked down upon the devastated remains of the Stancik Ranch.

It seems my loves are nought but a fleeting phantom amid the shadows of time. God, please grant me the strength to live once again.

THIRTY-ONE

AS THE DAY CAME TO A CLOSE, MARY, HER SIX CHILDREN, AND Henry ate a scant meal of sweet potatoes and boiled eggs. Many weeks had passed since Vaclav's departure, and now his name was seldom mentioned among family members.

"Mrs. Mary and Miss Julia," Henry said, "thank you for supper. I think I will go check on the goat and chickens and retire for the night."

He stood up and pushed his chair against the table. Julia glanced at her mother and then looked at Henry.

"Mama wants to know if you need more blankets or anything, Henry."

"No, Ma'am," he smiled. "But thanks for asking. I will sleep just fine. Good night, All," he said with a wave of his hand. "I'll see you in the mornin'."

"Good night!" Joe and Frank chorused as he passed through the door and shut it behind him.

"I like Henry," Frank said. "He is nice to me."

"He is nice to me, too," Joe replied. "As a matter of fact, I bet he likes me better than you."

As Frank stood up to contest the statement, Mary laughed and motioned for both of them to leave the kitchen. After the dishes were clean and put away, Mary and the girls joined the quarrelsome boys of the family in the living room.

The flames from the fireplace felt warm and cozy against the chill of the winter night. Julia organized a game with the other children, while Mary sat down with a needle and thread to darn stockings.

Suddenly the children jumped up and ran to the window. Julia glanced out and ran to her mother.

"Horses are approaching!" she said. "It sounds like they are running hard."

Mary put her mending to one side and joined the children at the window. Two men dismounted and tied their horses to the wagon. They were laughing and talking loudly as they walked up the steps to the house.

"Pa!" Julia told Mary. "It is Pa and another man. They act like they are drunk."

Seconds later, the door flew open, and Vaclav entered with an empty whiskey bottle in one hand. He stumbled across the living room, ignoring the happy shouts of greeting from the youngsters. Mary hurried to his side and put her arms around him, but he shoved her away with such force that she fell against the fireplace. Before she could raise herself to a sitting position, Vaclav was astraddle her.

The Stancik father appeared demented to the startled youngsters as he leaned close to Mary's face and shouted, "I don't need you! I have a lot of women in town."

The statement was followed by crazed laughter.

"Lots of women, Mary," he shouted. "Women who can talk and hear!"

Mary was devastated. Her heart was broken. Oh, how she wished she had never learned to lip read.

As Vaclav backed away from her, she struggled to sit up.

"Why are you yelling at her?" a deep voice said with a chuckle. "I think she's a pretty little gal!"

Vaclav glared at the big man standing in the doorway. The stranger tossed his whiskey bottle in a corner of the room and staggered toward Mary.

"If you think she is so great, you can have her," Vaclav snarled as he stepped aside.

Mary glanced at her terrified children and tried to struggle to her feet, but the stranger was on top of her before she could move. With teeth, fingernails, and lashing arms and legs, Mary desperately fought the attacker, but her size and strength was no match for the massive drunkard.

Oh, how I wish the barn was closer to the house, she heard herself thinking. *Perhaps Henry would have heard the commotion and already come to investigate.*

Suddenly, Mary saw Joe run toward them with a log in his hand. Before the man could react to Joe's whack on his shoulder, Frank leaped on his back. As he struggled to fling the boy off, Julia, little Mary, and Carrie began to beat him with a broom, coal shovel, and fists. He rolled off Mary and crawled across the floor until he was able to stand up. He staggered through the doorway.

Seconds later, Julia turned from the window and hoarsely announced, "He is gone."

Vaclav fell to his knees beside Mary.

Shaking his head, he said, "I'm sorry. You know I wouldn't have let him hurt you. You are my wife."

Mary gasped as she felt his hand moving slowly across her breast. Once again, she felt herself pinned beneath the weight of a man. She fought to be released from his grip, and suddenly he fell to one side, grabbing his head. Joe was standing over him with the log. As the father raised up and reached for the boy, Frank and the girls again joined the battle.

Mary stood up and watched as the barrage of household weapons followed the fleeing Vaclav through the door and into the night. The youngsters did not re-enter the house until they were convinced that he would not return.

Nestled within the covers on their bed that night, Mary tried to induce feelings of hate within her toward Vaclav for his lewd behavior. Tossing and turning, she fought the sensitive compassion and adoration for the man whom she had bonded with for twelve years. Finally relinquishing inner turmoil to exhaustion, she relaxed her head against the cool pillow.

Indeed, one day, she finally convinced herself, *my Vaclav will return with the gentle goodness and caring that he once maintained. On that special day, I will heal him with my love, and we shall be as one.*

For the next several days, Julia did not let Mary from her sight. Not one of the children spoke of the embittered battle against the two drunken men, nor did they mention their father's name. Mary honored their choice; she, too, made no mention of the controversial incident—even to Henry.

Many nights later, the drunken friend of Vaclav's returned as a thief in the night. Mary awakened with the huge intruder standing beside her bed. Even though she was subjected to this horror, she managed to reach the pistol that lay next to her pillow. She cocked the gun and pointed it toward the shadow in the moonlight. The man, shocked upon seeing the shiny object, fled from the house. Mary could not move from her position but held the cocked gun ready until the light of dawn appeared. Upon the new day, she wept.

Later that same morning, the door of the Stancik house suddenly flew open, and Julia raced across the yard toward the barn.

"Henry!" she yelled. "Henry, come quick! Mama wants you to hitch the team to the wagon."

The hired man walked over to the corral fence and leaned on it as he answered in a calm, slow voice.

"Whoa, slow down, little gal. What seems to be the problem?"

"Mama says we are leaving this place right now," Julia replied breathlessly.

She watched as Henry came through the gate and pushed the board into the slot to lock it.

"She said to hurry, Henry. I don't know why she is so nervous and upset, but she woke all of us kids and told us to pack a few things."

Henry put his hand on her shoulder as they walked toward the house.

"Let's go see what that Mama of yours has in mind, shall we? Everything will be all right, Julia," he said soothingly. "I think that she is probably right. It's time to leave the ranch. The Lost Piney Woods is swarming with renegades and outlaws."

"I don't know what we would do without you, Henry," Julia grinned. "You have been a dad, a grandfather, and a best friend to us kids."

Henry affectionately ruffled the top of her head with his hand.

"Yep. It's been pretty rough putting up with you youngsters all of this time," he chuckled.

Julia nodded and grinned as he opened the door, and the two of them entered the house.

Thirty minutes later, after being informed that they would be heading for LaGrange in hopes of finding Vaclav, Henry was loading the wagon with Stancik belongings, while Mary and the children gathered what was left of the eggs and vegetables. After stowing the last of the family's goods in the rig, he tied their goat Rosie to the tailgate. Henry laughed as Turban jumped on top of the tarp that covered the possessions.

"You won't be left, old fellow," he said. "Them boys may forget their mama or baby sister, but they won't forget to take you."

Turban licked his hand as he walked by on his way to the barn.

Minutes later, he emerged from the structure, leading his horse. He tied his bedroll behind the saddle and stepped into the stirrup.

"C'mon, Chub," he murmured to his mount. "Let's get that deaf lady and her youngsters to LaGrange."

He nudged the horse with the heels of his boots, and Chub began to trot across the barnyard toward the team and wagon.

Henry, the friend and compatriot of the forsaken Stancik family, heard the whistle and felt the thud of the arrow as it sailed through the air and entered his chest. He was aware of a searing heat as his body slumped over the saddle, and he slowly fell to the ground. His breathing narrowed to short gasps. He barely heard the whoops of renegade Indians approaching from the east.

The boys, who were now standing at the wagon, ran back inside to warn Julia. Mary ran toward the hen house to shield the girls. One Indian rode past her, grabbing and pulling her onto his horse. He held her tightly around the waist. She was no match for him but continued struggling. In desperation, she kicked and scratched, and somehow managed to work her way loose from his grip. She fell to the ground exhausted.

Hysteria had set in, but only for a moment, as Mary composed herself for her children's sake. She could not stand, but crawled toward the house. Julia's scream of anger was immediately followed by a volley of rifle fire which quickly frightened the enemy away.

Henry struggled to rise, but his vision suddenly blurred. A deafening roar resounded within his head, and then, the world was silent, lost amid the shadows of unconsciousness.

THIRTY-TWO

MARY AND THE CHILDREN WERE AWAKE EARLY THE NEXT morning digging a grave. The grave was for Henry. During the night he had died in Mary's arms with part of the arrow still piercing his chest.

Julia's voice now echoed amid the stillness of the newly dug grave.

"God, please take good care of our friend Henry. You will find him to be a good man. Thank You. Amen."

"Amen," her brothers and sisters quietly repeated.

"I hate them Indians!" Joe declared in a loud voice.

He wiped the tears from his face with one sleeve and kicked at a rock with his boot.

Mary placed Henry's hat on the crude wooden cross they had fashioned before motioning for the children to follow her. She climbed up on the seat of the wagon and took the lines in her hands. Julia helped the younger children into the back before taking her place alongside her mother where she laid the rifle across her lap and checked the supply of ammunition. As Mary slapped the lines against the horses, the wagon lurched forward and rolled down the dirt path.

After the wagon steadied, Julia asked, "Why should we go all the way to LaGrange to try to find Pa? He doesn't want us."

Mary handed the lines to her daughter to free her hands for signing. "Watch what you say, young lady! He needs us."

"How do you know that, Mama? He has not even come home for weeks, and last time he did . . ."

Mary put her hand over Julia's mouth. She shook her head and jerked the lines from the girl's grip.

The miles slowly passed beneath the woman and her six children as the team and wagon traveled along the rough dirt trail toward LaGrange, Texas.

One late cloudy afternoon many days later, Julia suddenly pointed to an abandoned shack among a cluster of oak trees not far from the trail.

"Shall we stop there for the night, Mama?" she asked. "It looks like a storm is coming and this is one time we are going to need some shelter."

Mary nodded and reined the team toward the dilapidated structure. Raindrops pelted the ground as the little band quickly unloaded Mary's trunk from Austria and the scant supply of food. Julia unhitched the team and tied them and the goat beneath the large oak trees, while Mary, Carrie, and Joe secured the tarp over the holes in the roof of the cabin. Little Mary and Frank organized the interior, although periodically stopped by fits of ambition from Millie and Turban.

Lightning streaked across the evening sky, followed by a distant rumble of thunder as Mary, Julia, Carrie, and Joe entered the makeshift enclosure. After a meal of raw vegetables, peanuts, and goat milk, Mary and her offspring crawled beneath comforters to sleep. But their night of rest was frequently shattered by the wrath of Mother Nature, lashing out at the Texas countryside. Bolts of lightning cracked time after time near the little shack. Deafening blasts of thunder bellowed above a torrent of rain. The young children snuggled closer to Mary and Julia with each eruption of light and noise. And thus, the forsaken Stancik family endured yet another night away from the only home that they had ever known.

"Henry told me that we will travel southwest," Mary signed to Julia the next morning after her oldest daughter had awaken. "He said there is a big river to cross. We should be near that river now."

"Yes," Julia agreed. "He told me the same thing. He was hoping that we would have good weather. He said that the river is impossible to cross if it floods. He said if it was in flood stage that he would build a ferry and . . ."

Suddenly Julia shuddered and walked to the doorway. With her arms hugging her waist, she stared at the raindrops that were pattering upon the pools of water near the shack. Mary quietly watched her oldest daughter for a moment.

My dear Julia has lost a very dear and sweet friend, she reflected. *My thoughts have been on my problems, while my child has suffered alone. Oh how I wish that I could take away her pain!*

Mary stepped beside Julia and put her arm around the young girl's shoulder. Julia slowly turned and looked at her. Mary gazed into her tear-filled eyes and nodded.

"It is good to cry," Mary signed and embraced her.

And thus, within the confines of an abandoned shack in the middle of a strange territory, the mother and daughter grieved for Henry and shared fear for the morrow.

As mid-day approached, Mary noticed the clouds dissipating overhead. She motioned for Julia and Joe to follow her outside.

"Your aim was very good the other day, Julia," she signed. "Would you and Joe like to hunt rabbits rather than Indians today?"

The sister and brother grinned at one another.

"Yes, Mama," Julia said.

"Then go get your rifle," she signed. "And, Joe, you get the ammunition. You two be careful and return before sundown."

Throughout the afternoon, Mary watched over the younger children. Little Mary and Carrie held the lead ropes of the horses, allowing them to graze, while Frank baby-sat the goat. Mary systematically draped wet garments and blankets on the limbs of nearby trees, while Millie tottered around with Turban.

The afternoon passed quickly and pleasantly with the little group venturing into the nearby thickets for berries and nuts, but, as the sun approached the western horizon, Mary felt concern rising within her over Julia and Joe.

I hope they return soon, she mused. *Real soon!*

"Have you heard gunfire or your brother and sister yelling?" she signed to little Mary and Carrie.

"No, Mama," they replied.

"Do you want us to look for them?" Carrie inquired.

"No!" Mary signed in an agitated motion. "I do not want any of you to leave this shack!"

Suddenly little Mary, Carrie, and Frank ran to the doorway.

"What is it?" Mary signed furiously. "What do you hear?"

She was unable to get their attention, so she finally tapped Frank on the shoulder and repeated the question.

"Gunshots, Mama," he responded. "We heard two gun-shots."

Mary sighed in relief before signing, "Good. Perhaps Julia and Joe have killed us a rabbit for supper."

Frank quickly repeated the optimistic message to his two older sisters. Mary picked up Millie and followed the young-sters through the doorway.

Several minutes passed before the mother saw Julia and Joe running toward them. Neither one was carrying a rabbit, and both seemed frightened as they raced toward her. She put Millie down and signed, "What is it? Are you all right?"

Julia struggled to catch her breath before saying, "Snakes, Mama. We found the river that Henry mentioned but the flood has washed the snakes into it."

Mary motioned for the youngsters to enter the cabin. After allowing time for them to be seated, she signed, "You are both all right, aren't you? You did not get bit?"

"No, Mama," Julia said. "We didn't get snake bit. And we didn't see one rabbit either."

"The river is full, Mama," Joe interjected. "And the water is muddy and rolling fast."

"It is about one mile from here," Julia said. "Henry said that it usually takes two days after the rain stops for the water to recede."

Mary struggled to subdue the disappointment that was building within her. She gazed at her two children and slowly shook her head.

"We must have patience and faith," she signed. "The river will go down, and we will travel on to LaGrange. But," she smiled, "for now, we have a partial roof over our heads, and we will eat nuts, berries, and the last of our vegetables. We will be fine, my dear Julia and Joe. We will be just fine."

Three days later, the nervous family again hitched up the team, stowed their belongings, and crawled aboard the wagon. Julia grinned at her mother as she sat down beside her. Mary winked and smiled when the girl calmly placed the rifle down on the wagon bed and leaned against the sideboard. The mile long journey to the river was relaxed and fun for the youngsters as they played with Turban and talked to the goat who was trotting along behind the rig.

Mary felt a lump rising in her throat when she reined the team to a halt at the river's edge. For the first time since losing her hearing, the Baroness felt grateful that she was unable to listen to the world around her.

The sound of rushing water may dissolve what little courage that I have left, she decided.

With the whip in one hand and the lines in the other, Mary commanded the team into the river. As they slowly moved into deeper water, the pull from the wagon grew more intense. Time after time, Mary's whip fell on the rumps of the horses as they struggled against the force of the water. The perpetual surge of the river hit the sides of the wagon, forcing it to slip sideways. She dared not remind herself that she had never learned to swim. She was numb with fear, but she knew she had to appear brave for the sake of the children. She leaned forward, encouraging each step of the team. They leaped against the double-tree, straining for every inch toward shore until their hooves finally settled on firm footing.

After reaching the safety of solid, dry ground, Mary halted the team and looked at Julia.

"We must rest the horses," she signed. "They are exhausted."

Besides, she thought, *I am not sure that I can hold the lines any longer. If I was standing up, my knees would be knocking together!*

Mary sat in the wagon and watched the children run and play until she regained sufficient strength to climb down from the rig. Then she slowly walked over to the nearest oak tree and sat down. A moment later, Julia joined her.

"Where are we, Mama?" Julia asked.

Mary looked around to see if any of the other children were nearby before signing, "I honestly do not know. We have taken a southwest route since leaving the ranch, so I feel that we are okay. But, Julia, right now I have no idea how far we are from LaGrange."

"I wonder if Pa will be surprised to see us," Julia smiled. ". . .if he is even there. Do you think he has missed us?"

Mary smiled and nodded.

"I am quite sure that he has missed us very much," Mary signed.

As her mother closed her eyes and leaned back against the tree, Julia left to find her brothers and sisters.

Minutes later, the girl returned in a run. She fell to her knees and grabbed Mary's shoulders.

"Mama, wake up!"

Mary looked at her oldest child and frowned.

"What is it, Julia? I am very tired. Please let me rest for a little while longer."

"It's Joe and Frank, Mama," Julia replied excitedly. "They heard church bells ringing. The sound came from the other side of that hill!"

Mary leaped to her feet and followed the girl toward the top of the incline. After reaching the summit, her heart suddenly pounded with excitement. Her eyes focused on a beautiful sight. It was a town which was divided by a wide street. Its numerous buildings were adorned with painted signs and banners. Tall oak trees and foliage in bloom added warmth to the scene. At the opposite end of the street, a small white church glistened beneath the rays of the mid-morning sun. Many horses hitched to buggies were tied and waiting for the parishioners to return from Sunday services.

Mary embraced her children and signed, "At least we now know what day this is. Sunday!"

The youngsters squealed and raced back down the hill toward the wagon. Julia walked beside her mother.

"What town is it?" she asked.

"I don't know," Mary signed. "I am just thankful that we are in civilization again. Perhaps someone there can tell us how to get to LaGrange."

The exhaustion and heavy burden of responsibility disappeared as Mary climbed upon the wagon and retrieved the lines.

Vaclav is a fine husband and a wonderful father deep within, Mary mused as she slapped the rumps of the team with the lines. *I am certain now we will find him soon and he will help us relocate in a safe and happy haven. I will help him. Together we will build a new home for our family.*

While the wagon slowly moved toward the town, Julia tried to clean faces and brush the hair of her younger charges. With meager possessions stowed in a weather-beaten wagon, Mary arrived with her children, two tired horses, a dog named Turban, and one very gaunt goat called Rosie. But, hope and happiness now overshadowed the doubt, pain, and dread of yesterday as the forsaken Stancik household lumbered onto the main street.

And thus, Baroness Mary and her siblings withdrew from the untamed territory of the Lost Piney Woods and entered a civilized Texas town to begin life anew.

THIRTY-THREE

"THE SCHOOL HOUSE, MAMA," JULIA SAID. "JOE AND FRANK want to see the school house."

Mary smiled and nodded as she reined the team to a halt in the school yard. Everyone quickly jumped down from the wagon and ran across the playground. Mary trotted after them, while Julia followed with Millie in her arms.

Seconds later, the older children were standing in front of the large stone building.

"Look, Mama," Frank said as he pointed toward the roof. "What is that?"

"That is the school bell, Frank," Mary signed. "The schoolmarm rings it in the mornings to call the students to class. She rings it again at the end of recess to call the pupils back into class."

Mary felt a tug on her skirt and looked around. Joe was standing beside her. His eyes were sparkling with delight as he pointed toward a window.

"Look inside, Mama," he said. "There is a long blackboard on one wall, just like you always told us about!"

Mary quickly walked to the glass aperture and peered inside. For a moment, she could smell the chalk dust and feel the soft black eraser in her hand. Visions from her youthful school days and tutorship at the Austin School for the Deaf poured forth, and she inhaled deeply to absorb the pleasant memories.

A few minutes later, the little band again climbed into the wagon.

"Where are we going now, Mama?" Julia inquired.

"We are going to find some hot food and plenty of it!" Mary signed with definitive motions.

After traveling half-way down the main street, Mary suddenly stopped the team in front of a tall building. She pointed to a sign above the entrance.

"LaGrange Hotel!" Julia read in a whisper. "Look everybody!" she yelled to her brothers and sisters. "We are in LaGrange."

After taking the team and wagon to the livery stable and removing funds from the Austrian trunk, a grateful Mary led her family into the hotel dining room. Julia ordered ample food for the seven of them before walking to the front desk to reserve sleeping quarters.

"How many are in your party?" the desk clerk inquired.

"Seven, Sir," Julia responded.

The desk clerk studied the register for a moment before looking at Julia.

"That will require two rooms at least," he said.

"No!" she declared in a firm voice. "We must all stay together. One room will be sufficient."

"But there are not enough beds in one room," he argued, "to accommodate seven people."

"Just put additional beds in that one room," she requested. "We have traveled a great distance, and we will not be separated now."

Minutes later, she rejoined her mother, brothers, and sisters at the table.

"We have a room," she informed Mary.

"Did you have any trouble with sleeping seven in one room?"

"No, Mama," Julia replied. "Everything will be ready and waiting for us."

Moments later, bowls of hot and steaming mashed potatoes, gravy, carrots, and pinto beans were set on the table in front of them. A platter of thickly sliced ham and another of fried chicken soon followed. The family's eyes widened as hot, freshly-baked bread, butter, and sliced tomatoes were added to the feast. Talk was limited to requests for more until the bowls and platters were virtually empty.

"That was good!" Joe commented.

"Yes it was," Mary signed.

"The vegetables don't taste like yours, Mama," Carrie complained. "They are too mushy."

The children laughed until Julia raised her hand to silence them.

"Carrie," she patiently explained. "We have been eating our vegetables raw. Remember?"

"Oh," Carrie whispered. "Guess I forgot."

With tummies full and spirits high, the anxious family patiently waited for their room to be readied. Within a short time, Julia was summoned to the front desk and soon returned with a key in her hand.

"It is ready," she told her mother.

"Good," Mary signed. "I am so tired. I hope everyone will want to retire early this evening."

She looked at the sleepy-eyed children around her and smiled.

"Somehow, I don't think there will be any problem getting cooperation."

As they entered their quarters, Julia nodded her approval. The room had been altered to wall-to-wall beds and pallets.

"This will be just fine," Mary signed. "You are an excellent spokesperson for me, Julia. I don't know how you talked the clerk into accommodating all of us in one room."

"I just handled it like you would have, Mama," Julia grinned.

Mary smiled and kissed her on the forehead.

"I thank you, my child," she signed. After yawning, she added, "I think that I will go to bed. I feel very tired."

As dusk faded into the darkness of night, the room settled into a peaceful silence. The Stancik family slept, void of hunger, stormy weather, and renegades. They slept with the knowledge of unity and security close at hand.

The following morning, Mary told little Mary and Carrie to watch the younger children.

"Julia and I have business to attend to for a while this morning," she explained with hand motions. "We will not be away from you any longer than necessary."

Ten minutes later, the mother and daughter were standing at the front desk, awaiting response from the clerk.

"Vaclav Stancik," Julia repeated. "He has often spoken of LaGrange. And I am sure that he has been staying at this hotel. Do you know him?"

As the man behind the desk nervously shuffled through the registration book, Mary glanced around the lobby. A tall, buxom lady was standing near the door, staring at them. She seemed to be listening to every word that Julia was saying. Mary smiled and nodded at her. The lady responded by approaching the desk and asking Julia about her inquiry.

"Did you say that you are looking for Vaclav Stancik?"

"Yes, Ma'am," Julia responded with a smile. "He is my father."

The woman paused for a long moment before quietly inviting Julia and Mary to join her on the couch in the lobby area.

"I know the man that you are speaking about," she said in a low voice as they sat down.

"Are you his only child?" she asked, looking at Julia.

"No. I have five brothers and sisters," she replied. "And this is my mother, Mary Stancik. Mama is deaf and cannot speak," she added, "but she can read your lips."

"I see," the lady looked at Mary and asked, "How long have you and Vaclav Stancik been married?"

Julia watched her mother's hands and then relayed the message, "Over twelve years."

"I see," the lady said quietly. "I am Madam Hannacek. I am from Austria. You must understand why I interfered with your inquiry at the desk. I have a story to tell and you must hear it. Twenty-six years ago, I married a handsome young man. We had three children and a fourth on the way, when he was suddenly drafted into the Austrian Army."

"But what does your husband . . ."

Julia's question was interrupted by Mary.

"Please, Julia," she signed, "let her finish."

"Forgive me," Julia murmured softly. "Please continue."

The dark haired woman cleared her throat before saying, "He became a deserter when our fourth child was due to be born. He came home and hid in the attic of our house, but Austrian officials informed me that our entire family would be in jeopardy if we aided in his desertion. Therefore, Vaclav was forced to leave his home and homeland in disgrace. Although we learned that his destination was Galveston, Texas, America, we did not know at the time if he arrived safely. Twenty years we waited for his return. He never came. Our son, John, grew to manhood and became a priest. He decided to serve the deity in a Texas chapel. This choice allowed him to both serve God and search for his father."

Mary touched Julia on the shoulder and slowly signed, "Has your husband been found?"

Julia started to interpret the hand signal, but Madam Hannacek stopped her.

"Several weeks ago, my son was called to the LaGrange Hotel to perform last rites on a dying man. Father John recognized him immediately. That dying man was his father." She paused briefly and looked at Mary before quietly adding, "And your husband Vaclav, Mrs. Stancik."

Julia gasped. "My father is dead?"

Madam Hannacek quickly shook her head.

"No, Julia," she said. "He is now slowly recovering. My son had summoned me to America in hopes that I may see him before his death. I arrived over one week ago and found him in an improved state."

Madam Hannacek suddenly stood up and walked over to Mary. She leaned toward her and gently touched her on the shoulder.

"Vaclav finally confessed to me about his current situation. He didn't say much, but he *did* tell me that he had taken on another family. He loves both of us, Mary, and he loves his children. However," she added softly, "you and I both know that his second marriage is invalid. He must never return to you and your children. By law, he belongs to his first family. Painful or not, we intend to get him back!"

Mary felt numb. She could not believe she had spoken the vows of matrimony with another woman's mate. Now she understood why Vaclav had been so hesitant and bewildered on their wedding day. She stared at Madam Hannacek as though she was seeing a ghost. As though in a trance, she slowly shifted her gaze to Julia, but the young girl did not look at her.

Moments later, the first wife of Vaclav Stancik turned and walked through the lobby of the hotel. After speaking to the clerk for a brief time, she started up the stairs and quickly disappeared from view.

Julia touched her mother on the cheek.

"Let's go, Mama," she suggested. "I will help you to our room."

As the moon cast shadows upon the deserted streets of LaGrange, Texas, Mary wept. Her grief for Vaclav was as great as her sorrow had been for Rudolph many years before. The sweet, kind, and caring father of her children was dead in her heart, and she knew not her destiny.

I am so very tired, she thought, her head aching unmercifully. *It seems that happiness is but a fleeting second amid the hours of sorrow. Once again, I find myself alone, a forsaken and forgotten casualty of love.*

She glanced around the room at the slumbering children. Each one was peaceful and content within private dreams and hopes and desires.

What beautiful children I have, Mary suddenly noted. *I am so fortunate to have healthy, intelligent children! How could I possibly feel alone and abandoned when I am surrounded with their love.*

Her gaze turned toward the mirror above the bureau, and she solemnly studied her moonlit reflection within the darkened room.

I am still rather young and attractive. As Countess Larisch would put it, this strange twist of fate is merely another adventure in my life. I will return to the Vecera Estate with my family and begin life anew. Oh how wonderful it will be to see Papa, Frances, Marie, and Annie again! They will love my other five children as they did Julia.

And thus Mary charted a new course for her and her children. Hope and happiness was once again on the distant horizon, a new beginning for the Stancik family in that beautiful house near the town of Muldoon, Texas.

PART III

THE RETURN OF
BARONESS MARY VETSERA

MULDOON, TEXAS
AMERICA

THIRTY-FOUR

THE NEXT DAY, MARY FELT EXCITEMENT MOUNTING WITHIN her as the team and wagon approached the path that led to the Vecera Estate.

Julia glanced at her mother and grinned.

"Are we almost there?"

Mary's eyes glistened with renewed life, and she pointed toward a large white house that was now intermittently exposed amid the trees.

Oh, Papa, Mary thought, *it will be wonderful to see you again. So much has happened in my life, and yet the barn, the corrals, and your fine selection of horses seems the same.*

With childlike enthusiasm, she quickly slapped the lines. The horses responded by trotting toward the house with ears forward. Her heart pounded as she spotted her father waving and running down the steps of the veranda. She dropped the lines and jumped down from the wagon. She felt safe and secure as her father embraced her. After a moment, he backed away and put his hands on each side of her face.

"Welcome home, my dear daughter," he said excitedly. "But what on earth are you doing here?"

"Thank you, Papa," she signed. "I shall explain later."

Tears streamed down her face as she added, "It is truly wonderful to be home."

Suddenly her hands darted in a flurry of jumbled words.

John laughed and walked over to the side of the wagon where Julia was quietly holding the lines of the team.

"Hello, Grandfather," she said with a smile. "Do you remember me?"

"Do I remember you?" John laughed. "Julia, my little granddaughter, crawl down from there!"

As her feet touched the ground, John hugged her.

"You have grown up since I last saw you, Julia, but we have never forgotten our little granddaughter. You have become a very pretty young lady!"

"Thank you, Grandfather," Julia said, blushing amid the praise.

Moments later, Mary stood beside her father, proudly watching as Joe, little Mary, and Carrie jumped down from the wagon and embraced their grandfather for the first time.

"We are missing two!" Mary suddenly signed to Julia.

The girl giggled and squeezed her mother's hand.

"Don't worry, Mama," she said. "I am sure that we will find them."

They walked to the back of the wagon and peered down upon the stacks of belongings. John laughed and pointed to Frank who was curled up beside the Austrian trunk, sound asleep. The dog was nestled against him, and he raised his head when Mary and Julia woke the youngster. With a yawn, Frank rubbed his eyes and jumped from the wagon.

Mary stepped back and folded her arms across her chest, savoring each precious moment of the scene as her youngsters gathered around their grandfather.

I *have dreamed of this moment*, she thought with a satisfied sigh. *And now this moment seems like a dream. A beautiful dream.*

"Come inside," John chuckled. "Marie and Ben are visiting us, but they went into town. They should be returning soon, however, and when they discover you have arrived, they will want to grace us with an extended visit. And Annie—she will be coming over within the hour."

Marie and Ben "visiting?" she asked herself. *And Annie "coming over?"*

"Marie will explain after she returns," John said in answer to Mary's puzzled expression.

"Where is Frances?" Mary inquired with her hands. "Is she all right?"

"Her rheumatism has kept her in bed today, Mary, but I am sure that your presence will ease the pain."

The excited Stancik children started toward the house, but Mary suddenly halted.

"Wait, Papa," she signed. "We are still missing one!"

John and Julia followed her to the wagon where they soon found Millie, nestled upon the little pallet that had served as her private bed. A smile depicted pleasant dreams as she napped.

"Now, how could we forget this little girl," John questioned.

He gently picked her up and held her in his arms. Now *everyone* began walking toward the house.

Later that afternoon, Mary and Julia were upstairs with the young children when Marie burst excitedly into the room. She grabbed Mary, and the two embraced.

"Mary, how wonderful it is to see your face," the Countess said as she released her grip on the Baroness and gazed into her eyes.

Mary looked down without replying.

"I can see that life has not been easy for you," Marie stammered, "but at least you are home now."

Then she turned to the oldest offspring of the group.

"And this must be our little Julia! You have grown into a fine young lady."

The Countess proceeded to greet the other children before she turned her attention back to Mary.

"My name is Mrs. Ben Freidrich now, Mary," Marie smiled. "That whistling Vienna cabby and I finally became very good friends, which eventually grew into a loving relationship. We have been married for some time now and have a place in Ganado."

"Are you happy?" Mary signed eagerly.

"Very," she responded with a broader smile. "And now, let's get the youngsters ready to meet their grandmother. John is helping her prepare for the introductions, and she will be waiting for all of you in the sitting room."

As the two groomed and dressed the youngsters, Marie related portions of events that had taken place since her last letter to Mary.

"After the Empress returned to Austria," Marie said. "she was in the country for some time visiting her daughters before Franz Josef caught up with her. He begged her to return for good, but when she refused, he ordered her out of Austria and his life forever. She later received word of her own death and burial. The Emperor reported that she had been stabbed in the heart with a hat pin, which gave Frances quite a start. She felt that he could have found a more dignified route for her demise. Reports from Vienna stated that she had a stark and unambiguous funeral, which allowed the Emperor to culminate the feigned death without question."

"Has she been feeling poorly?" Mary signed.

Marie nodded.

"John often carries hot water for her to soak the joints that are aching from the rheumatism. Ben has taken Frances and I to the train station several times so we could make trips to the spas in Hot Springs and Eureka Springs, Arkansas, and also to Galveston Island to find relief for her pain. We enjoy going, but it eases her misery only for a while. These are times she wishes her Vienna psychiatrist, Dr. Josef Skoda, was near to give her a mental boost. She told me how ironic it was that she could take the rough seas and never get sick, climb mountains, walk marathons and not complain, ride horses in strenuous hunts and find pleasure. But the one thing she needed most, the love of a human, she was most afraid of."

"And, how is Annie?" Mary signed. "I get the idea she doesn't live here anymore either."

"She is doing great," Marie replied. "She is married now too. She still comes over to visit. But, mainly she still comes here to take care of John and Frances. I have the distinct impression that she is spoiling them. In fact, since Ben and I have been visiting, she has certainly spoiled *us*. Seriously, I do not know how anyone would manage without her."

A gentle rap on the door interrupted the conversation. The Countess opened the door, and John's smile greeted her.

"Frances is downstairs, waiting to meet with her grandchildren," he said.

Sixteen-year-old Julie, tall and majestic, descended the stairs first. Admiration was obvious in Elizabeth's face because Julie was her wonder child, a true princess, a daughter of her son. They gave each other the warmest of embraces.

Little Mary and Carrie would not walk separately, so hand-in-hand they came down together. Little Mary was taller and stood more erect than Carrie, while Carrie, so sweet and lovable, smiled and showed her dimples.

Frank and Joe could not contain themselves. They started down before their time, skipping every other step and almost overtaking their sisters.

Elizabeth had quite a time with the four of them around, each hoping to be hugged first.

Meanwhile, Countess Larisch had given her attention to little Millie to insure that she would make an impression on her grandmother. Millie was close to three years old but had yet to master steps very well. Marie carried her down proudly and place into her grandmother's arms.

Frances was so filled with joy she could not even speak. Mary, walking with her noble elegance, went to her, and for the first time endearingly embraced her not as a stranger, nor an empress, but as a mother.

Thus, Empress Elizabeth met her six Stancik grandchildren in an orderly manner, befitting the nobility that she was. The children's presence for the time being was gladly accepted. Both grandparents were grateful because now they knew there would be joy and laughter in the house, something they had all forgotten since Mary and Julia had been away.

During dinner that evening, the conversation was light-hearted, and the children felt love and security within the family tenor. As the youngsters finished eating, they were excused from the table. Finally, Mary was alone with her Austrian family. She stood up and walked to Frances.

"I am so happy to be with you again, Mother," she signed.

Tears streamed down the face of the matron as she embraced the deaf lady standing beside her.

"I love you very much, Baroness Mary Vetsera," the Empress murmured. "I am glad that you came home."

She smiled warmly, then walked over to her father.

"Thank you, Papa," she signed. "I cannot express my gratitude for your acceptance of me and my children. We had no other place to go."

He held her hand as her eyes shifted to each face at the table.

Bradfisch, she thought, *you have become a special friend and invaluable ally to the Vecera family. And my dear friend Countess Marie, you have stayed beside Empress Elizabeth, maintaining the status of friend and collaborator since your departure from Vienna. And you, my sweet Agnes, have never forsaken any of us. Even after marriage, you continue to serve as a loyal and dedicated maid. And Empress Elizabeth, my dear mother, how wonderful it feels to be in your presence once again. How fortunate I and my children are to have you all!*

Each person at the table seemed to read her thoughts, and each one smiled and nodded as her gaze shifted slowly from one to another.

She kissed her father's hand before departing from his side.

"I will put the children to bed now," she signed. "I love you, Papa. Good night."

Thus, seven lives were unified and accepted into the home of John and Frances Vecera. As Mary settled into bed within cool, clean sheets, it seemed as though her past years in America were nought but a dream. Time was lost as she gazed through the open window at the moonlit gardens below.

Perhaps I will indeed find love and happiness again, she told herself.

Mary then smiled and embraced the pillow beneath her head before closing her eyes in peaceful slumber.

THIRTY-FIVE

LIFE ON THE VECERA ESTATE SOON SETTLED INTO A COMFORTABLE routine. Mary spent numerous hours playing games with the children, even allowing little Mary and Carrie to brush and braid her hair each evening. The dark locks had grown until the ends touched the floor when Mary was seated, which granted the girls a chance to test their creative skills in hairstyling.

Mary could not have loved her children more. She couldn't speak the words "I love you" but she didn't have to, for their daily hugs and kisses indicated that.

Shortly after Mary's return, the three older girls were enrolled in school. John quickly assigned himself the task of taking them to and from class. He enjoyed the youthful enthusiasm and cheerful company of Julia, little Mary, and Carrie as they traversed the familiar route each day. Upon their return in the afternoon, Joe and Frank welcomed them home, begging their sisters to share each and every detail of their day.

Soon Mary became concerned over the discrepancy of the last names of her children. To put her mind at ease, John and Frances made a trip to the courthouse in LaGrange to give them all the legal name of Vecera.

From the moment of arrival, Countess Larisch felt a motherly bond for Millie. And thus, Ben and she took the little girl when they attended church and social functions in the community. Life seemed so serene and normal that no one was aware of Mary, slowly slipping into pages from her past.

One afternoon, Mary entered her room and donned the white gown that she had worn at the ball in Vienna. A festive ambiance of royalty and music by Mozart danced within her mind as she left her quarters and walked slowly down the stairs. Murmurs of appreciation for her beauty, poise, and grace echoed from within latent memories as the deaf woman nodded and smiled at the phantom images from her past.

Baroness Mary Vetsera smiled as the vision of Crown Prince Rudolph appeared. She graciously accepted his outstretched hand and gazed into his eyes. The handsome, young Prince placed her hand on his arm, and he proudly escorted the beautiful Baroness toward the ballroom.

And thus, Mary glided across the main floor of the Vecera Estate, lost within the visions of her past. Moments later, she entered the garden, twirling and dancing as though encompassed within the arms of Rudolph.

Joe and Frank were playing nearby when their mother suddenly appeared. Frank watched her for a moment before giggling and pointing at her.

"Look at Mama, Joe," he said. "She's dressed funny."

Joe watched her dance among the colorful foliage. Her long, white gown made a rustling sound as she swayed to the music within her mind. Suddenly, she was plucking the delicate blossoms, holding each one against her cheek for a moment before casting it aside.

"Wait here, Frank," the older boy ordered.

He stood up and walked toward his mother, who was now leaping among the colorful plants. After catching up with her, he gently tugged on her skirt, but she did not seem to notice him. Tears streamed down his face as he again pulled on her vestment.

"Mama!" he yelled. "Mama, what is wrong?"

He circled around until he was standing in front of her, and this time, he grabbed her hand. As though awakening from a trance, Mary blinked her eyes several times before focusing her attention on Joe. She kneeled down beside him, brushing the tears from his face.

"What is the matter, my son?" she signed.

"You were dancing and picking flowers and you have on a fancy dress," Joe sputtered.

Mary laughed and embraced the boy.

"No, Joe, I was only chasing a butterfly," she signed. "You must stop worrying so much."

Joe nodded, but he did not look at her eyes before slowly turning away.

The four oldest Stancik children later attended school to study catechism in preparation for first and second communion within the Catholic doctrine. Annie stitched the garment for each child, taking pride in each carefully sewn white attire. Although Mary had been denied requests to attend church on prior occasions, Frances granted the mother permission to attend the children's communion.

"But you must cover your face," the Empress quickly demanded.

"It has been many years since the assassination," Mary argued with darting gestures. "I do not want to wear a disguise!"

"But you must, Mary," Frances contended, "or you will not attend the children's communion ceremony. It is much too dangerous for you to be seen."

And thus, Mary did indeed attend the communion; her face cloaked within a veil of secrecy. Although a large brimmed bonnet served as a camouflage against recognition, the requirement became an additional catalyst for living in times past. Amid tears of pride, pain, and inner-turmoil, she observed her children as they proudly walked with the procession from the school to the church. The beauty of the well-groomed, handsome youngsters was tarnished only by the whispers of vicious rumor among the elderly women in attendance. As the children cast petals from the flowers in their hands, Mary's mind again traveled back to sweet and happy times in Austria. Indeed, the visions of admiring glances eased the torment of critical reality.

As the days grew into weeks, however, the constant noise and play of the children began to take its toll on Frances. Her physical pain was enough torture in itself, but the deviant household routine had all but done her in. This, combined with Mary's regret of the past and the fact that handling the children seemed too much even for her to handle at times, created conflict between mother and daughter. Arguments arose with disquieting regularity over the smallest and most insignificant matters. Even another trip to Hot Springs with Marie didn't seem to offer much solace to Frances.

After dinner one evening, John, Elizabeth, Marie, Ben, and Mary were relaxing in the sitting room of the Vecera home. The flames in the fireplace cast a pleasant glow and warmth—and in this rare moment, Mary's and Frances's discrepancies seemed at peace. The children were asleep, and the five adults basked within the serenity of the moment. Frances leaned back in her chair and puffed contentedly on her pipe as John and Ben discussed the current market for horses.

Marie's throat suddenly tightened as Frances rested her pipe on the table and leaned toward Mary. She caught herself wishing that the Empress had not earlier presented to her intentions about a less than pleasant matter—a matter that she sensed was about to be set forth.

"We must discuss the future of your children," she said in a firm voice.

"What about my children?" Mary signed. "They are very happy and healthy."

"Indeed, they are," Frances replied. "and I love them all dearly. But they need a mother and a father, and John and I are too old to rear another family."

The room suddenly felt cold and hostile to the deaf woman. She glared at the matron before signing, "What do you mean? I am their mother."

"True," Frances nodded. "But what would you and the children do without the help of your father and me?"

The Empress did not wait for a response. Rather, she sat straight and regal as her strategy unfolded.

"I have given this a great deal of thought," she continued. "There are couples within this community who want children. They are financially stable, and the children would have good homes."

Mary rose to her feet. Her body felt like a coiled spring as she absorbed the words spoken by her mother.

"You are asking me to give my children away?" her hands darted. "Never! *Never!* They are my life. How could I ever begin? No, I could never do that. I couldn't. I won't."

John quietly stepped between the two women. His expression openly displayed surprise and concern.

"Frances, don't you think that this action is a bit severe?"

The matron looked at John before reverting her attention back to Mary.

"I see no other solution. Mary is incapable of supplying the children's welfare and education. They must be granted the opportunity to live in a normal and stable environment."

"I will not give my children away!" Mary repeated in frantic hand gestures. "You cannot make me forfeit my motherhood."

"I can, and I will," the Empress replied in a calm manner. "The children deserve a home, both parents, and a good education. We are unable to provide these needs."

Mary fled from the room, and Marie followed her. Within the confines of Mary's bedroom, the Countess embraced the distraught mother of six. After allowing her time to calm down, Marie gently pushed the hair from her face and smiled.

"You are not showing disfavor by sharing your children," she said. "You are offering them a benevolent chance for happiness within a family unit. Do you recall that day not long ago when you had been allowed to wait with your children at the train station while your mother and I returned from Arkansas? Remember how you were fighting off a woman with your purse who tried to take Frank? She wanted him very badly, Mary. She had no children of her own, and she would have given him a wonderful home. She even kneeled and begged, offering to pay for him."

Mary shuddered as the vision of her son being led away surfaced. She felt the pain of forfeiture arise within her bosom as she recalled Frank's brother and sisters jumping in to pull him from the grasp of the woman.

"But," Mary signed.

The Countess interrupted the hand signal before Mary could continue.

"Believe me Mary, my dear friend, it will be easier once you let the first one go. You just as well start with little Millie. Ben and I love her very much. We must be leaving soon and we will be honored if you allow us to adopt her into our home. She will fill the emptiness that Ben and I feel for the children that we had to leave behind."

Mary looked at Marie for several seconds before slowly nodding her head. Her hands trembled slightly as she signed, "I think Millie would be very happy with you and Ben."

"Very well," Marie said. "You must remember, Mary, that there are a number of good couples, eagerly awaiting parenthood. And, your release from parental responsibility will grant you the freedom to marry. Although Frances seemed harsh, her decision indeed offers a fair and honorable solution for you and yours."

Indeed the separation had to begin—and so it did on a gray, windy day. Little Millie, attired in her best white dress, was clasped tightly in her mother's arms. Through tears and a terribly heavy heart, Mary kissed her daughter from cheek to cheek, again and again.

As Marie approached Mary and reached for her child, Mary managed to tear herself away with the deepest of grief. With unbearable pain, Mary could barely watch as her baby disappeared. Helplessly she ran up the stairs, tearing at her clothes in anger, until she submitted to the bed and slept.

The Countess felt intense sorrow for Mary, but what hurt the most was the guilt she held inside for playing a part in injecting misery into Mary's life once more. The best she could do now was to promise occasional visits.

After Ben, Marie, and Millie left the Vecera stead, Mary and her mother fought bitterly over the decision. Tension mounted within the household as Mary frantically gestured her wrath upon the intrepid matron of the home, but her protests were to no avail. Plans were set into motion for the adoption of Julia and the five Stancik siblings.

The reality of a separation of such magnitude was indeed overwhelming for Mary. But somehow she summoned the courage to deliver the bad news. With tears streaming down her cheeks, she gathered the children around her. She spoke of the loving home and new hope, emerging on the horizon for each of them. With sorrowful hearts, the mother and her children shared both tears of loss and faith for the future.

Even John could no longer ignore the undeniable truth as he helplessly watched his daughter's anguish. With an aching heart, he helped Mary to the dinner table. But not much food was eaten.

And thus, one cool morning in the town of Muldoon, Texas, it came to pass that Father Cromchek devoted a portion of his

Sunday service to the Vecera grandchildren. The reverent plea for good homes was indeed destined to be answered, and the division of mother from child and child from brother and sister would soon be scheduled to commence. The bond of family unity and love would then shower forth upon the Texas countryside, and, once again, Baroness Mary Vetsera would be able to do nothing but weep for lost love.

THIRTY-SIX

THE DAYS PRIOR TO THE DEPARTURE OF THE CHILDREN WERE filled with torment for Mary. Each day, as the mother wept openly in front of her siblings, they withdrew to the out-of-doors under the pretense of playing but instead huddled against the side of the house, sobbing.

Julia was next to leave. Mary felt a part of herself die as she embraced her oldest daughter. How could she ever do without her? Silence befell the two. No words were needed for this parting. Not a tear was shed

It was now well into spring before Mary was forced to face her next good-bye. The nights still demanded a fire and Mary looked snug in the cozy living room. Frank and Joe, who had already been promised their new home, had only a few days left to enjoy their family. Mary tried to look busy with her needle point. But her eyes were fixed more often than not on the two sons that had brought her so much joy and laughter.

Several times during those remaining days, as she had on a number of other occasions, she found herself coming to Joe's rescue whenever he was trying to make music with the accordion he had been given at Christmas. His arms could hardly reach the keyboard so his mother would get behind him and help hold it up. As she placed her hands on his, she could feel the vibrations and enjoy the beautiful music.

Mary let the boys stay up and play longer than usual on their last day home. They took full advantage by wrestling on the floor. Soon she could resist it no longer and put away her needlepoint to join them. She got a little ruffled but she didn't mind, rather she enjoyed it.

Time slipped away and it was soon well past the boys bedtime. They became weary and sat quietly next to each other, watching the low flames which now were barely flickering. As Mary sat beside them, the fire reminded her of someone gasping for his last breath. That was exactly the way she felt. The next time she turned her attention to the boys, she found them asleep with their heads on her lap.

The next day, Mary was staring out the window of her bedroom. *I do not wish to live,* she brooded. *I am very weary. My only two sons are gone and my life no longer has purpose. Dear God, please have mercy on my tired and grieving soul.*

She turned and studied the white gown that she had laying across the bed as though contemplating her return to fantasy. After a moment, she shook her head and turned back to the window.

Little Mary and Carrie are still with me. I must remain strong for them. Perhaps, she decided, *no one will call for my two daughters, and we can remain together.*

The slim thread of hope brought a faint smile to the lips of the distraught mother. As she left the room and descended the stairs, her poise and manner was that of a determined woman and a dedicated and benevolent mother. She passed Frances, who was seated in a chair on the veranda, and walked straight to the garden. Carrie and little Mary approached their mother and looked up at her with concerned expressions.

"Hello, Mama," Carrie said. "Are you feeling better to-day?"

Mary embraced each child before signing, "I am fine. I am just fine."

The girls were delighted when they saw their mother smile for the first time in many days. She kneeled beside them and began to pull a few weeds from the flower bed. Throughout the remainder of the afternoon, Mary shared the beauty of nature with her two siblings; a colorful butterfly, the amazing strength and stamina of a laboring ant, and the grace of a bird in flight. Beneath the warm rays of the late autumn sun, the trio basked within a loving bond of labor and laughter. Together they sat quietly on a log near the house, savoring the peaceful moment at hand.

Early evening was upon them when little Mary and Carrie suddenly stood up and pointed toward the east.

"What is it?" Mary signed.

"A horse and buggy, Mama," little Mary responded.

"It looks like the Father," Carrie added. "Why would he visit us this late in the day?"

Little Mary giggled and said, "Maybe he is hungry, Carrie. Annie will have dinner on the table before too long."

Mary felt like someone had hit her in the stomach. Instinct warned her of the impending loss of her last two children.

No God, she inwardly screamed as tears once again filled her eyes. *Not little Mary and Carrie too!*

Carrie knelt down in front of her mother, and, trying to wipe the tears away, asked, "What is wrong, Maminka? Can I help you?"

Mary gazed upward and pointed toward the heavens, saying, "Only God can help me now."

Her daughters embraced her tightly as little Mary said, "My Maminka, we shall never let you go!"

Mary tried desperately to hold onto her last shred of hope. But, as they slowly walked toward the house, she was sure of the reason for the unannounced call by the parish priest. A home had been found for her two remaining children, and Mary knew that she could weep no more. Her eyes were void of emotion as she watched Frances receive the news. Mary ascended the stairs as though in a trance. She entered her room, shut the door, and fell across the bed. The last wisp of hope had vanished from her life, and she again experienced the void of purpose in living.

When Annie came to check on her, Mary was in deep anguish. She signed, "Must I see the torture in their eyes as our arms are pulled apart?"

There would be no good-bye at all this time. She ran to the barn and hurriedly rode her horse away. She remained absent until she was certain they had left.

Mary tried to nurse her grief like a glass of vintage wine. However, she soon withdrew from reality, frequently donning the white gown and waltzing among the flowers in the garden and nearby fields. John, Frances, and Annie watched her deteriorating mental state, but none of the three realized the gravity of her condition.

Mary was seated on a chair on the veranda one morning when Father Hannacek unexpectedly approached the house. He tied his horse to the hitching post before slowly walking up the steps toward her. She did not look at him as he sat down beside her. After a moment, he turned her face toward him.

"I must speak with you, Mary," he said. "It is about Vaclav, my father."

Suddenly the priest saw a glint of comprehension within her dark and lifeless eyes. He reached into his coat pocket and retrieved a folded piece of paper.

"This is yours, Mary. It is a letter from Vaclav."

Mary accepted the paper, and her hands were surprisingly steady as she unfolded and read it.

> My dearest Mary,
>
> I have come here to our home to try to rearrange my thoughts. But all I see is you and our precious little ones. I am filled with joy when I remember our many happy and wonderful days together. But that joy never lasts. I now only have my whisky to sustain me. Without you, I cannot

go on. My heart is breaking. My will to live is gone. Please forgive me for I hold you dearly in my heart.

The message was signed by Vaclav.

Mary looked at the priest, but she made no effort to communicate.

"He is dead, Mary," Father Hannacek said softly.

Mary tried to follow his every lip movement as he explained the circumstance of the death.

"He was invited to stay with my mother and sister after his recuperation, but he insisted on returning to Lovelady and the home that you had shared. After an extended length of time, I rode to Lovelady to check on him. I found this note beside his lifeless body."

Father Hannacek put his hand on Mary's before adding, "He loved you very much, Mary. I felt that you should know this."

He stood up and slowly retraced his steps to the awaiting mount. Mary remained seated with the note clutched in her hand as the Austrian man of the cloth disappeared from the Vecera Estate.

After dinner one evening, Mary embraced her father before signing, "Papa, I would like to return to the Austin School for the Deaf. Teaching would give my life purpose again. Will you take me?"

"Of course, Mary," John smiled, "but I will not be able to leave until the work is done. Perhaps soon."

"Thank you, Papa," she replied in calm hand gestures. "Later will be fine. I will have my belongings in order and ready when the time comes to leave."

But fate again destroyed Mary's plan for a new and useful life. Before the seeds grew strong roots, violent storms with heavy rain demolished all chances for a crop. The journey to Austin was delayed until the fields were again sown. By the time the crops were resown, ripened, and harvested, winter weather and rain was upon the Texas countryside. The planned trip to Austin once again was postponed.

Meanwhile, Mary was falling deeper and deeper into a dark and dangerous depression. She refused to communicate with the family, but she shared her thoughts on paper in letters to Countess Larisch.

One day, not long after thanksgiving, she returned from a horseback ride in a fitful mental state. She went straight up to her room and sat down at her writing desk. Her hands trembled as she wrote.

My Dearest Countess Larisch,

Now that my adorable children are all gone, I am without words. My grief is unbearable. I am tormented daily as I can only embrace my dear ones in my heart. The only solitude I get from this tragedy is knowing the children are well and happy in their new homes.

My mother insists that its best I do not see them often as the hurt would only deepen. Once when Mama and Papa went to church, however, I hid in their wagon, hoping to chance a glance at my darling ones. But the opportunity never came. I did want so desperately to go inside the church. I needed to be around people. But, of course, I was forbidden to do so. Oh what a desolate life.

A few times, I have taken my horse and rode him close to the church, although I always stay back when the service is over so no one will see me. I go in the back in the cemetery, where the tall trees, shrubs, and tombstones hide me. There I stand and pray in hopes of getting a glimpse of my children. The last time I was there, my whole being was threatened with grief and despair. I felt like a thief in the night, abducting my own flesh and blood into my heart. I not only left many tears, but left my very

> soul. I felt as if I had already been buried and wished that it was so.
>
> On the way home, I passed a tiny one room church attended by the blacks. I could not hear them singing, of course, but I sensed their praises by their movements. Their arms were reaching out in a spiritual fervor which I had never before seen. As I stopped to watch them, I wondered if they would still be praising the lord if *their* children had all been taken away. How long must I keep suffering? Will the haunting of Mayerling ever let go? Even now must it do away with my motherhood when I need my children so? What am I to do, Marie, what am I to do?

Mary paused and rubbed her eyes. She was growing weary but she still had much to say. Sharing her misfortune with Marie was the only thing at the moment that was enabling her to maintain a grip on sanity. She continued in a nervous scrawl.

> I finally got to go on a trip to town, but not even that was without its price. Papa could see how depressed I was, so he asked if I would like to go with him to purchase the winter supplies. I was thrilled beyond words, for how many years had I waited patiently for that moment. I could so vividly imagine seeing stores, churches, banks, boutiques, and people.
>
> I sat in front of the wagon with Papa most of the way. As we approached town, though, Papa insisted I go to the back of the wagon and cover up for he said I should still not be seen. I did peak out several times and so much enjoyed seeing the town.
>
> Papa kept carrying out supplies from the general store and placing them around me. I begged to go inside but he refused. When he finished loading, he asked me to be patient a while longer. He wanted a beer, and the saloon

was inside the hotel. He stopped the wagon right in front of the hotel's boutique. In the window, the mannequins seemed to beckon me, as they displayed the most beautiful dresses.

I suppose I forgot myself, and stood up in full view. Suddenly, I was approached by a man who had come out of the saloon. He started to talk to me and I became frightened. He went back into the hotel and returned with a friend. His friend looked at me and said, "Yes she's a beauty." They came closer and reached out for me. I struggled and pulled back the best I could. My dress got torn. I was horrified. Thank God Papa came out at that moment. He was angry and shouted for them to get away. The men just stood there and one said "Ah, no wonder you're hiding her. She's the prettiest thing around here. You want her for yourself." My father assured them I was his daughter but the men didn't seem to believe him. Papa finally had to pull out a pistol to chase them away.

Papa didn't have to explain to me why I never got to go anywhere before nor did he have to remind me that this would be my last trip. Even though I enjoyed the trip, I could not keep from being saddened by what happened—sad for Papa having to go through this kind of turmoil.

I had planned to return to school, but I haven't even been able to do that. The trip has been canceled time after time. I meet the train almost daily. The engineer and I have established a routine of waving as he goes by, which gave me an idea for getting back to the school. The last time the repairmen were at the train tracks, I handed them a note which stated that I would appreciate a ride to Austin as I wanted to go to school. When they realized that I could not hear nor speak, they laughed and made fun of me. I tried using sign language, but they just mimicked my hand gestures and laughed more. As I watched them leave, I felt that my soul had been taken from me. I write of this because I know that you will understand my thoughts, dear Marie. I love you and hope you, Ben, and Millie visit soon.

Mary quickly signed the note and slipped it into an envelope. She did not move from the writing desk until the sun was below the western horizon. She felt imprisoned within a body that was destined to suffer the torments of hell on earth. The effort of living was an overpowering burden, too painful to endure.

Several weeks later, Mary's depression suddenly turned to rage, and one evening she vented her wrath upon her mother.

"It is your fault that Rudolph died," she signed in rapid hand gestures. "How were we to know that I was conceived out of wedlock by the regal and noble Empress of Austria and Queen of Hungary? Our love for one another was pure and true, and your deception fired the gun that killed Rudolph! And you not only took away my Rudi, but you sent my children away as well."

Frances flinched with each bitter accusation. When Mary received no response from her mother, she turned her vengeance to the absent Countess Larisch.

"And Marie," she signed, "is as guilty as you! Perhaps she helped with the assassination of the Crown Prince. As active liaison and confidante for Rudi and me, she was granted the needed information from the beginning! I hate you, and I hate Countess Marie Larisch, and I hate my life!"

The unexpected outburst stunned not only Frances, but John and Annie as well. As Mary ran from the room, the three looked at one another, but, for a full minute, no one spoke. The aura of shock diminished as John stood up and walked to Frances. He kissed her on the forehead and held her hand.

"She is emotionally upset this evening, Frances. Tomorrow she will be over her anger."

Frances sighed and nodded her head.

"She is right, John. It is my fault that my son is dead. I should have told the truth many years ago."

"Don't say that," John said in a firm voice. "I have wished many times that I could turn the hands of time back, but we can't. Blaming yourself will not erase the past. I, too, could have prevented the tragedy from occurring, but self-reprisal will be of no benefit to anyone now."

Frances gazed up at John and affectionately patted his hand.

"You are a fine man, John Vecera," she said softly. "I have no doubt that my survival depends on you."

"May you live for many years, Frances," he smiled.

John tossed and turned on his bed that night for two hours. He was unable to dispel the angry scene with Mary from his mind. He moaned softly and abandoned the disheveled bed. Quietly descending the stairs, he walked through the dark and silent house, stopping only after reaching the veranda. The severe winter night felt cold on his brow, but the air smelled fresh and clean. He gazed into the starlit heavens and slowly shook his head.

"I will never understand why there is so much pain and sorrow in the world," he grumbled. "If each adverse incident in our lives teaches us a lesson, my daughter must have the wisdom of Solomon. Please bless her, Lord."

The posture of John Vecera was that of an aged man as he quietly re-entered the house. He ascended the stairs and paused beside Mary's closed door. Although expecting to hear signs of restlessness, the soft sound of sleep drifted from within the chamber.

And thus, for the remainder of this night, John Vecera no longer shouldered the heavy burden of pain within his daughter. Once back in bed, he closed his eyes, feeling intense gratitude for this brief moment of respite.

THIRTY-SEVEN

JOHN AND FRANCES WERE EATING BREAKFAST THE FOLLOWING morning when Mary entered the dining room. They exchanged a fearful glance before John spoke.

"Good morning, Mary. How are you feeling?"

"Much better, Papa," she signed.

She walked over to Frances and hugged her.

"Please forgive me," she gestured. "I honestly do not know why I was so angry with you and Marie last night."

Again, John and Frances glanced at one another, but this time relief was evident in their visual contact.

"Please," Frances said, "sit down and join us. Annie prepared a fine breakfast this morning."

"No thank you," Mary signed as she glanced toward the clock. "I think that I will ride my horse for a while this morning. I enjoy waving to the train engineer as he passes, and I will miss him if I take the time to eat now."

"Very well, Mary," John smiled. "Mr. Brown will saddle your horse for you. Have a pleasant ride."

"Thank you, Papa," Mary smiled. "I will."

She kissed her parents on the cheek before leaving the room. As the front door closed softly behind Mary, Frances looked at John.

"At times I feel that two different people live in her body," she said.

John nodded in agreement before adding, "I believe that three or four would be a more accurate count."

Fifteen minutes later, they heard a horse, loping away from the estate.

During the following weeks, Mary's journey to the railway on her horse became a daily ritual. And, with each passing day, it became more and more apparent that depression was once again an atrocious, unseen adversary within her. Soulful cries echoed through the stillness of night within the Vecera home, and tears of grief filled the hours of each day. Frances felt a sense of relief sweeping over her each morning as Mary left the house for her daily journey to the railway.

Christmas was almost upon them when John brought a welcome letter from town. He quickly tied his horse to the hitching post and ran up the steps to the veranda. Frances met him at the door.

"You seem excited, John," she smiled. "Did you receive good news while you were in town?"

"I think so," he grinned. "I think that we received a letter from little Mary and Carrie."

He gazed around the room as he handed the letter to Frances.

"Where is Mary," he asked. "I was hoping that she would be here when I returned."

"I haven't seen her since she left on her horse this morning," Frances replied. "She should be coming in soon though."

The grandparents quickly read the correspondence. The message relayed the news that little Mary and Carrie would be arriving shortly to spend Christmas with their mother.

"That is wonderful," John responded happily. "Perhaps their presence will grant Mary happiness through the holidays."

"Yes," the Empress agreed. "Perhaps they will. I have been very concerned about Mary's state of mind, fearing that

Christmas may be too much for her to bear without any of her children."

As John walked toward the kitchen, he grinned and said, "I will go tell Annie that we are having guests for Christmas. Sometimes I think that she misses those youngsters as much as Mary."

Several hours passed, but Mary did not return to the Vecera Estate. John paced back and forth in front of the barn while the sun cast longer and longer shadows across the Texas terrain. Suddenly the sound of a running horse caused him to breath a sigh of relief and smile.

"Thank God," he declared. "I am glad that she is home at last."

But his relaxed attitude was shattered as Mary's horse halted in front of the barn without his rider. John caught the reins in his trembling hand.

"Mr. Brown!" he shouted. "Saddle two horses. And hurry!"

Moments later, the two men were mounted and ready to search for the missing rider.

"John," Frances yelled from the veranda. "What is wrong?"

"Mary's horse came home without her," He replied in a loud voice. "We are going now to look for her."

Without further explanation, John and Mr. Brown kicked their horses into a lope.

Less than one fourth mile from the house, John saw her prone body, lying on the ground.

"Mary!"

He jumped off his horse and ran to her. She was face down upon the damp sod, sobbing and groaning.

"Mary, are you hurt?" John asked breathlessly. "Did your horse throw you?"

As John picked her up, she shook her head. But, the moans and sobs did not subside as he carried her limp body to the house. He gently laid her down upon the couch, and Frances placed a pillow beneath her head.

"What happened?" Frances inquired.

John placed his fingers on his lips to silence the question. Frances nodded in understanding and put a damp cloth across the deaf woman's brow.

"We have some wonderful news for you," she said.

Mary looked at her without responding.

"Little Mary and Carrie will be coming to spend Christmas with you."

A faint smile appeared on Mary's face, and, a moment later, she sat up.

"Is it true?" she signed. "Are they really coming to spend Christmas with me?"

"Yes," John smiled. "Here is the letter. Read it."

Frances and John watched their daughter read and reread the message. With each perusal, new life seemed to filter through the dark depression.

"They will be arriving tomorrow!" Mary signed. "We must make preparations for them. Annie and I must decorate the house."

"That's right," John chuckled softly. "We don't have much time before they arrive."

That afternoon, while Mary and Annie planned their decoration strategy, John and Frances snuck into town to buy their unexpected guests some gifts.

The following morning, John and Mary left the house at dawn to find a tree befitting the holiday season. Upon their return two hours later, Frances met them at the door.

"My heavens!" she gasped as they struggled to carry it inside. "That is a huge Christmas tree. I haven't seen one as big since my young days in Possenhoffen. The poor horses. You should have used four to pull it instead of two."

"Mary picked it and she would have no other," John chuckled.

"Well," Frances replied, "with a tree that lovely, we should have one fine Christmas."

That afternoon, Mary stood by the window anxiously awaiting the arrival of her little girls. The moment she spotted the carriage, she ran down to meet it without even bothering to put on a jacket. On such a happy occasion, she had become oblivious to the cold. With outstretched arms, she sprinted alongside the carriage as if she was readying herself to pull them out before it stopped.

John and Mr. Brown had just finished setting up the tree and when the girls came inside, they got too excited about decorating, even to rest. They were impressed with a tree that was so enormous it barely fit the room. It was so big, in fact, that Annie and Elizabeth kept busy for quite some time making decorations. Mary and the children worked diligently to fill every limb. Then the candles were lit. Enthusiasm reached its peak when Mary climbed the ladder to put up the star. There was more tinsel at the bottom, but the beautiful garland that rested there gave it no word of mention.

Annie and Mary brought in the gifts and the little girls eagerly placed them under the tree. It appeared that the happy picture was complete, but no so. Among the laughter, chatter, and warm hugs and kisses, no one noticed the occasional absence of the distraught mother. Mary's other children were at the forefront of her mind. She couldn't help but wonder what kind of a Christmas they were having. Wishing for a sudden miracle, she thought, *maybe they are still coming today; maybe they want to surprise me*?

She ran to the window many times but it was late and darkness had already overtaken the day. There would be no more children coming.

Mary helped her daughters into bed early. Midnight was rapidly approaching, traditionally the time for the gifts to be opened. She stayed in the bedroom, dreading the thought of leaving her daughters alone even for a second. Sitting near them, she felt their cheeks, stroked their hair and simply watched their every breath as they slept. Ever so often she turned and quickly looked around, as if she expected to see the other children there near her.

When she finally *did* leave, Mary approached Annie and with her wordless gestures said, "This bit of joy is going to end again when I have to tear myself away from a daughter's arms. How can I watch this grief on their innocent faces, knowing their hearts are breaking as they ride away?"

Midnight arrived, the girls were awakened, and came down in their long white ruffled gowns. The candles on the tree cast a warm glow all over the room. The fireplace flickered in contrast, trying to claim its own accolades. They stared with amazement as John and Mr. Brown rolled in a barrel of fruit.

Carrie and little Mary soon sat proudly amid the torn paper, hugging their identical dolls. Frances puffed contentedly on her new pipe, and John donned his new smoking jacket. Mary expressed her appreciation for a hand-made cross fashioned by Mr. Brown, a book of poems written by the Empress, and a set of pillow cases embroidered by Annie.

When the barrel of fruit was opened, John laughingly announced to Frances, "Help yourself. I know how much you love fruit. But please do try to save enough for a fruit salad tomorrow."

They all chuckled and the girls insisted on a juicy red apple.

The memorable night culminated with a gentle Bohemian Christmas carol. Frances smiled appreciatively and winked at John as Mary's two daughters sang each word without accent or flaw. It was truly a holy night.

No one, however, perceived the burden of sorrow in Mary's heart as she stole those precious moments to gaze through the window into the ebony night, wishing her other children could be present. Indeed, if one had, perhaps the former debutante of Vienna would have relinquished a portion of her pain. Alas, the world would never know.

THIRTY-EIGHT

On Christmas morning of 1906, the dawn of the new day cast a golden glow of renewed hope upon the Vecera Estate. Mary felt a touch of life seeping within the dark, dank cloud of depression as she donned a pretty dress for Early Mass. She assisted her daughters as they dressed, brushed their hair, and slipped into their Sunday shoes. Stepping back to survey the two youngsters, the mother smiled approvingly.

"You both look very pretty this morning," she signed.

"Thank you, Mama," they said in unison. "You look very pretty too."

"And, thank you," Mary signed.

The three curtsied to one another before leaving the room.

John and Frances were waiting in the sitting room as Mary proudly followed her two children down the stairs and into the gaily decorated area. John stood up and smiled as they entered.

"You all look very pretty this morning," he proclaimed. "I am honored in escorting you to church!"

Mary blushed with the warm praise, and the two little girls giggled.

"Thank you, Papa," Mary signed. "We will be honored to have you as our escort."

Frances stood up and faced Mary.

"You cannot accompany us to Mass, Mary," she said. "Rumors are plentiful, and your presence would only add to the gossip."

Mary's face turned pale, and her lips trembled.

"Frances, do not forbid my attendance at Mass on Christmas morning!" she signed.

"I am sorry, but you must stay home," Frances said firmly. "Your life could be in jeopardy if I allowed you to go. The church will be filled to capacity this morning, which would place you in a dangerous position. There may be some present with malice on their minds. No, Mary," the Empress repeated. "You cannot go to Mass with us."

The dark cloud of remorse again descended upon the Baroness as she watched John, Frances, little Mary, and Carrie settle into the seats of the buggy and disappear from view among the tall trees. Tears streamed down her face as she turned from the window and walked toward the stairs. She was on the third step when Annie suddenly touched her arm. The Austrian maid gazed into her eyes for a moment before embracing her.

"My heart hurts for you, Baroness Mary," Annie whispered. "I do not know how to ease your pain."

Mary collapsed on the step. Pent-up emotions poured forth as Annie sat down beside her. The Vetsera maid cradled the devastated woman in her arms until the racking sobs subsided. After regaining control, Mary sat quietly for a moment.

"Annie," she finally signed, "do you remember the other day when my horse returned without me, and Papa carried me from the field to the house?"

"Yes I do," Annie replied quietly. "I was concerned for your welfare."

"I had been to the church for confession.," Mary signed. "On the way, I almost changed my mind and I stopped to study the stillness of a stream. I thought that just like the water, my life wasn't going anywhere. Meanwhile, my innermost being was begging me to continue so I started riding hard. After seeing the steeple of the church, there was no turning back. As I approached, the father was on the church steps awaiting his confessors. With much happiness he motioned me in, for indeed my presence was a rare one, much overdue. I kneeled before the altar, praying for strength, guidance, and forgiveness. As I headed back home, my thoughts were jumbled and nonsensical. I urged my horse to run faster and faster, until I finally fell to the ground in a state of hysteria. I felt a desperate need to clutch the earth and cry."

I am so grateful, she thought, *that the tranquility I saw in the face of the Blessed Virgin Mary at the church crept within my heart as I made my peace with God. At least I now feel forgiven not only for all the iniquity from my past but for the sin that I have yet to commit.*

When Annie suddenly touched her damp cheek, Mary turned and gazed into her eyes.

"I cannot tell you the importance of my receiving communion," She signed, then resolved, *God forgive me, but there is nothing else that I can do now.*

Mary stood up and slowly ascended the stairs. Her body felt numb as she entered her chamber and opened the Austrian trunk. Her fingers trembled as she removed the long, white gown and gently laid it on the bed. Returning to the trunk, she removed a letter that she had written in Czechoslovakian to all her children that summer. Pausing a moment, she retraced the movement and retrieved another letter that was written in English and addressed to her attorney. She put both of them beside the gown.

Suddenly, Mary insisted on wearing the gown and asked Annie for assistance. She stood awhile in front of the mirror looking at her image, stroking her long hair, undoubtedly anticipating putting it up the way she had worn it in Vienna. She ran down stairs and onto the veranda, dancing and twirling in spite of the fact that it was chilly. Annie motioned for her to come inside, but Mary was totally oblivious to everything but her thoughts. Her radiant smile indicated that her heart and mind were enraptured in a beautiful memory. How could she ever forget that unforgettable night in a castle in Vienna, when her crown prince danced with her, and waltzed his way into her heart. She ran inside the house, but only for a moment, because the clock on the wall had beckoned her. It was time for the train.

Once again standing beside the railroad track, Baroness Mary Vetsera graciously accepted the offered hand of her beloved Crown Prince Rudolph. The vision of his handsome face smiled down upon her. The ecstasy of his love surrounded her in warmth and happiness. The train rapidly sped forward. Then Baroness Mary stepped onto the track. It seemed that, for an instant, her Crown Prince was indeed with her. But only for an instant, and then, Mary was no more.

EPILOGUE

December 25, 1906

Dearest Marie and Ben,

I do not know how to begin this letter. The flickering candlelight seems to disturb my thoughts. Today I write you with a heavy heart. My message is one of great sorrow as, on this day, we lost our dear Mary forever.

We will grieve for our loss, but perhaps our sweet Mary has found happiness at last.

God bless you and yours, my dear niece.

Frances

And thus, the princess, who could never be, found peace within an Austrian storm of treachery and deception.

In 1958, I, Irene Colvin, talked to Mr. Brown about the last few moments of Mary's life. He spoke in a calm, even voice as he told me of Annie, running through the field toward the railway on that fateful day after she realized what had happened. When the maid reached Mary, she sat down on the cold ground and cradled her mistress's lifeless body in her arms. Annie did not cry; she simply hummed quietly and caressed Mary's hair. He could not forget how Annie's arms had to be pried from the body of the Baroness.

"I was the last to see Mary alive," Mr. Brown related. "I had been in the field on my horse when I saw Mary running toward her usual encounter with the train. I didn't pay any attention, since this had become a daily ritual for her.

"The train must have been late," he added, "as she appeared nervous. She looked toward the end of the track, and then laid her cheek upon it to feel the vibrations that would tell her of the closeness of the approaching monster. As the train neared, she stepped back, but it was only a short step. I thought she stood too close to the track—closer than usual. She smiled and waved to the conductor. He smiled and waved back. The usual whistle was blowing when suddenly, without warning, the wheels began screeching unbelievably. I saw Mary in her white dress, almost floating, toward the heavy wheels."

He told me when my great-grandparents, Frances and John, returned from church with the granddaughters, they noticed the train was stopped on the track. Buggies and wagons were blocking the crossing that led to their house. People stared and whispered as the Vecera family approached, but no one offered an explanation for the strange occurrence.

Although Frances and John began asking questions, friends and neighbors turned away. John finally stepped down from the wagon to inquire about the delay. He walked toward the crossing to speak with the engineer.

Soon, he returned with an ashen face, clutching the side of the wagon for support and gasping, "It is Mary. There was an accident. Our Mary is dead!"

Mr. Brown went on to say that Frances embraced my Aunt Carrie and Aunt Mary. Tears of shock and grief then poured forth from each family member. It was indeed a tragic day for all of them.

I have long felt it to be equally tragic that the world was taught only to remember a young woman, a mistress who had apparently died in a double suicide with her lover. Now, however, everyone can know of the Mary that lived a secluded life in a small Texas town.

Mary was buried in a small, isolated cemetery near Plum, Texas. The gravestone simply reads:

> "Marie Vecera, born September 12, 1873, died December 25, 1906."

Meanwhile, a gravestone labeled "Mary Vetsera" still sits in the cemetery of Heiligenkreuz in Vienna. Included upon it is an epitaph chosen by Baroness Helene Vetsera, which was paraphrased from the book of Job, chapter 14, verses 1 and 2:

> "Man *that is* born of a woman *is* of few days, and full of trouble. He cometh forth like a flower, and is cut down: he fleeth also as a shadow, and continuth not."

Commencement of Research by Irene ZaSkoda Ward
July, 1948

Conclusion of Literary Manuscript by Irene ZaSkoda Colvin
July 8, 1994